Levant

A Champion Cornish Mine

by

John Corin

Edited and expanded

by

Peter Joseph

With contributions from

Kenneth Brown, Milton Thomas, Ron Flaxman
and Norman Lackford

Published by The Trevithick Society
for the study of Cornish industrial archaeology and history

© The Trevithick Society 2013

Second impression 2014

ISBN 978-0-904040-96-8

Printed and bound by R. Booth Print
The Praze, Penryn, Cornwall TR10 8AA

Typeset by Peninsula Projects
c/o PO Box 62, Camborne, Cornwall TR14 7ZN

DEDICATION

Introduction

The Trevithick Society first published John Corin's *Levant: A Champion Cornish Mine* in 1992. Since then it has gone through a number of revisions and new editions, most recently in 2010. Its continued popularity is proof of its abiding value, both as guidebook and popular history.

John's book appeared at just the right time. The only other history of Levant, by Cyril Noall, was by then scarce and expensive; furthermore it was much stronger on the mine's early history than more recent events. Crucially a number of volunteers were also beginning to see how the site at Levant might be made more accessible and interesting to visitors. So, successive editions of 'Corin' recorded the visual restoration of the preserved whim engine, the restoration of the boiler house and the engine's return to steam.

More recently the joint efforts of the National Trust and the Trevithick Society have resulted in a far greater appreciation of the entire area of Levant Mine and a great deal of new information has emerged. The time had come for a completely revised popular history of Levant, which would enable the visitor to make sense of this crucial site and its remains. Here it is, combining much of the pioneering work of John Corin and his collaborators with new information, colour illustrations plus a detailed map and self-guided walk. Thus the story of *Levant: A Champion Cornish Mine* continues, a fitting tribute to those industrial archaeology pioneers who saved Levant for posterity in 1935 and formed the predecessor of today's Trevithick Society, the industrial archaeology society for Cornwall.

Graham Thorne

for

The Trevithick Society

Acknowledgements
The help of Ron Flaxman, Anthony Power, Chris Quick and Tony Clarke is gratefully acknowledged.

CONTENTS

Chapter 1

Mining up to the 18th Century

It is not known when mining commenced in the St Just district but all historians agree that it is of great antiquity. Early to Late Bronze Age (c 3,000 to 600 BC) finds in Cornwall demonstrate that tin working was being carried out in several places, however it is not until the Iron Age that tin working in the St Just area can be demonstrated. Towards the end of the 4th century BC Cornwall was visited by Pytheas of Massalia (now Marseilles), a Greek explorer-cum-geographer. Pytheas is thought to have circumnavigated the British Isles and may even have reached Iceland. The writings of Pytheas have not survived, however the account given by Diodorus Siculus over 200 years later are regarded as being based on Pytheas. According to the accounts:

> The inhabitants of Britain who dwell about the promontory known as Belerion (*i.e.* the Lands End Peninsula) are especially hospitable to strangers and have adopted a civilised manner of life because of their intercourse with merchants of other peoples. They it is who work the tin . . . which they then melt down and cleanse of impurities. Then they work the tin into pieces the size of knuckle bones and convey it to an island which lies off Britain and is called Ictis . . . On the island of Ictis the merchants purchase the tin of the natives and carry it over from there across the Straits of Galatia or Gaul; and finally, making their way on foot through Gaul for some thirty days they bring their wares on horseback to the mouth of the river Rhone.

Chysauster Courtyard Village, about 10km east of Levant dates from this period and is associated with tin streaming; Carn Euny, 7km SSE and Caer Bran, 8km SE, are of the same period and near to tin producing areas. Moving into the Dark Ages, tin has been found at Chun Castle, just under 4km to the east and at Kenidjack Castle, 2.2km to the south-west; possibly another site lay on Cape Cornwall. In the 1950s, in a cliff working at Geevor, an oil lamp of the type used in Spanish mines in Roman times was discovered. This has been dated between the 4th century BC and the 7th century AD.

Possibly because Levant was primarily a copper producer in its earliest workings, the immediate area of the mine was ignored by those prospecting for tin. While a large number of tin bounds were registered in medieval times, none cover Levant. John Lelant, who travelled through St Just between 1534 and 1543, described the area as containing "no thing but a Paroch Church . . . and divers sparkeled Howses, the North Part ys Mountaynes and Baren Growne, but plenteful of Tynne". John Norden surveyed the area about 40 years later but also neglected the Levant area.

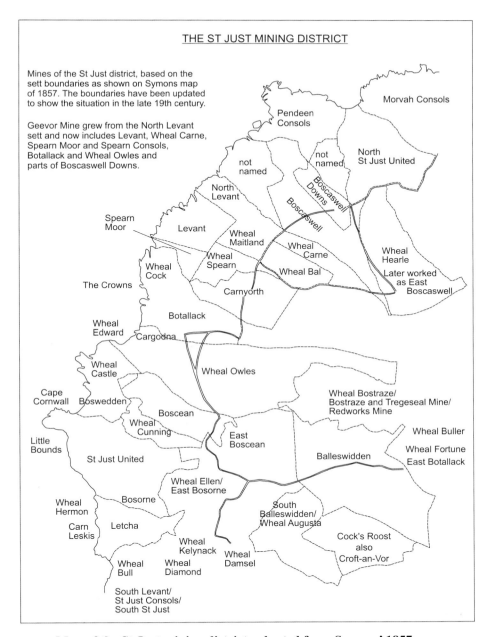

Map of the St Just mining district, adapted from Symons' 1857 map.

Cyril Noall has suggested that the name Levant came about in Elizabethan times, when the Levant Copper Company was set up. It is interesting to note however that the Crown is known as the "lords of the undersea leases of South Trewellard Mine", and it may be that Levant previously worked under this name. Trewellard Mine itself is marked on the 1842 tithe map at Trewellard Zawn, less than 500m to the north-east; this is probably the mine later known as Boscaswell Cliff Mine. Specimens of Levant ore were sent to Oxford in 1670 or 1680.

The St Just area was visited in 1724 by the Swedish industrial spy Henric Kalmeter, but his account also does not include Levant Mine, nor any of the mines which constituted it. It has been previously stated that Levant is named on Martyn's 1748 map of Cornwall, however this has been proved incorrect. The mine was working in 1793 when the first record of copper production took place, demonstrating that the old setts of Wheal Unity, Boscregan and Zawn Brinney had been amalgamated. However this was not a good period for Cornish copper mines because of competition from Anglesey, north Wales; the two mines here were producing almost as much copper as the total output of Cornwall at this time. Joseph Carne's 1822 geological map of the St Just district shows only Levant and "Zawnbrinny".

In 1891, Major Richard White is said to have told of Captain Joe Odgers, of Camborne, who prospected the lodes of Levant. An adit was driven inland and a shaft sunk 24 fathoms, but no mineral was discovered. Captain Odgers would kneel down in the level and lap the water, saying "I can taste the copper, though we can't find any". Joe Odgers was a 'colourful' character from Camborne and a friend of Richard Trevithick junior. Odgers was involved in a number of unsuccessful mining trials; in 1817 he was involved in an unsuccessful attempt to raise a sunken schooner from the channel leading to Padstow Harbour. In 1828 he decided to try his luck further abroad. Leaving England on June 4th, journeying from Plymouth to Portsmouth, then to Southampton and then reaching France via Jersey, he arrived over a week later. He worked on a couple of different sites during the year, producing samples of copper ore to show to interested parties. In August the following year he was peremptorily arrested and marched to St Malo, a 26-mile journey which took several days, where he was charged with forgery and swindling. After two trials he was acquitted; he unsuccessfully tried to sue his erstwhile mining company and returned to England on 23rd January 1830.

It has been suggested that the name *Levant* was derived from the former name for the area of the Eastern Mediterranean now occupied by Lebanon, Syria, and Israel. To this end it should be noted that the Treasurer of the Levant Company in 1824 was John Theophilus Daubuz, the brother of Lewis Charles Daubuz. The Levant Company, also known as the Turkey Company, was an English chartered company formed in 1581 to regulate English trade with Turkey and the Levant. A member of the Company was known as a *Turkey Merchant*.

Chapter 2

The Early 19th Century

In 1820* Captain Richard Boyns formed a company which included John Batten and Lewis Charles Daubuz, both men bankers and tin smelters, the former of the Trereife smelting house in Newlyn Coombe, as the largest shareholders. The mine was in 20 shares, and a call was made of £20 per share. Before this £400 was used up, a rich bunch of grey copper ore was cut and dividends commenced at once, a success probably not equalled in the history of Cornish mining: up to 1872 the mine would raise over a million pounds' worth of copper and tin, giving about £200,000 profit to the adventurers, the greater part of which was made in the first twenty years.

In 1822 the mine was 42 fathoms deep, the first level 12 fathoms below adit and extending 40 fathoms beneath the sea; part of it was stoped to 5 fathoms above the level. Another level extended 28 fathoms under the sea. Following the death of Richard Boyns in 1830 his shares in the mine were advertised for sale in the *West Briton*, where the mine was described as "for a considerable time past one of the most profitable Mining concerns in the County of Cornwall; and the present prospects, particularly in the bottom levels, are most flattering".

The first recorded accident at Levant came in 1834. On Tuesday April 10th a run of ground – a collapse – buried two men. Miners from other parts of the mine quickly set to work to rescue them, the work taking several hours. Fortunately the incident ended well with both men being recovered, suffering only from bruising.

In 1835 the mine acquired a 40-inch pumping engine from Harvey and Co. and the following year a 26-inch whim (hoisting engine) was acquired for Batten's Shaft, on the cliff below the present engine houses. By that year the shares had been re-divided and the mine was in 160 shares, on which £2 10s had been paid. A new lease of the sett, for 21 years at dues of 1-20th, had been obtained. Astonishingly the profits were averaging £1,100 per month, with a profit of about £8,000 a year over the past 10 years; dividends were paid bi-monthly.

In 1837 Levant sold only 56½ tons of tin for the year at £37 a ton however in 1838 some £37,000 worth of copper was sold, showing the dominance of that metal. The average price obtained £12 14s a ton, being the highest in the county and more than double that

*Writing in the 2nd volume of Transactions of the Royal Geological Society of Cornwall in 1822, Henry Boase stated that copper precipitation had been carried out at Botallack and Levant for "the last five years", implying an earlier opening.

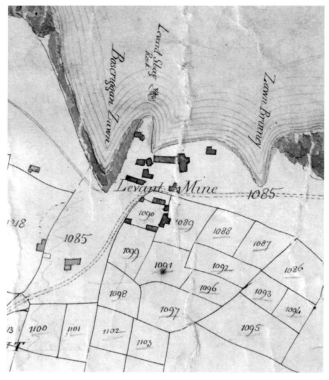

The tithe map of about 1841; what appears to be the 26-inch engine on Batten's Shaft can be seen on the right-hand side of Boscregan Zawn.

obtained for Cornish copper ores generally that year. A specimen ticketing paper dated November 29th 1838, showed that Levant had sold 85 tons of copper at £10 a ton and 65 tons at £16 9s 6d. At that time the wages of tributers west of Penzance averaged 47s 6d a month; tutworkers, 45s, and day labourers, 42s. In 1837 the mine employed 550 persons, and paid £1,500 in dues, of which £1,400 arose from copper. Balleswidden was then the only St. Just mine which exceeded it as an employer, 634 men, women and boys being employed there, while for many years Levant paid about one-third of the copper dues yielded to the lords by the whole parish.

In 1839 a new 21-year lease was granted to the adventurers. However the mine was only making small profits, with a monthly cost of about £1,800. Up to about this time all dues paid by the mine had apparently been received by the lords in whose land the shafts had been sunk. This year saw the mine's first recorded fatal accident. This happened when David Eddy, a "fine young man" of St Just was putting his tools into a kibble prior to descending a shaft. Somehow he lost his balance and fell 20 fathoms down the shaft.

It was in 1840 that Harvey and Co. of Hayle built and supplied the iconic 24-inch all-indoor beam winding engine that draws so many visitors to the site, other than the stunning scenery, of course. This engine was hoisting from Skip Shaft, to the rear of the engine house, from a winding drum outside the western side of the house. Skip Shaft is separated from Engine Shaft by just a few metres of rock but despite this the two are quite distinct. In March that year a man called Samuel Sampson, from St Hilary, was filling kibbles in one of the shafts. Losing his footing he fell 70 fathoms (420 feet) down the shaft where he was "literally smashed to pieces". The following month William Oats White was injured by boring a hole which had not exploded. Unfortunately the charge went off, doubtless caused by the drilling, and one of his hands was "so dreadfully mangled" that it had to be amputated.

In June 1840 another accident took place, when a young man was buried under 5 fathoms of rubbish (waste rock). After several hours the youth was eventually extricated by several of the miners. The young man was Richard White; later he was to become Major White and purser of the mine. It was said in later years that he had never worked underground in his life, however this incident shows that to be untrue, but it would certainly explain his unwillingness to ever work there again.

In April 1841 two men, Edward Nankervis, 33, and Thomas Gay, 29, were charged with fraudulently removing 2,000lbs of copper ore, to the value of £50, from Levant Mine, being the property of John Batten and others. One of the agents, Captain Ralph Goldsworthy, stated that for the past six months the two men had taken a pitch on a branch lode on the 140 fathom level, for 10 fathoms above and 7 fathoms in length, at 13s 4d in the pound. The pitch expired on March 26th, and on April 1st Goldsworthy had, on observing the pile of ore, been convinced that it could not have been raised in their pitch. The pile was 11 tons, about half of which was 'spangled ore', similar to that raised in the 120-fathom level, which the adventurers were working at 1s 6d in the pound. There were "no other ores in any other part of the mine like those in the 120", possibly the reason why the adventurers were working it.

The pile of ore, about 2 tons, had been examined previously by Captain John Trenear, who had not seen any of the spangled ore. However there was a scuttle-hole alongside the pile, leading to the 140 fathom level; this had not been examined because Nankervis had said that it was full of deads. On April 1st Trenear had been underground again and found that the scuttle-hole had been cleared, however in the crevices he found portions of the spangled ores. Ore from the 120 was thrown down to the 130, to be taken out on the tram-road that ran alongside the prisoners' pitch. It seems the two had helped themselves to about 2 tons of this ore and both were found guilty. The mine at this time employed 507 people and was still the second largest employer behind Balleswidden, Mine.

In 1841 the trustees of the estate of John Boase advertised for sale 10/160th shares in Levant. The advertisement waxed lyrical on the mine, stating that

It is quite unnecessary to enumerate to those Capitalists, who are acquainted with the Cornish Mines, the claims this Mine has on their attention, so well is she known as one of the most lucrative in the County; but, for the information of others, the following short sketch is presented. During the few years which the Levant has been worked, a clear profit of between £70 and £80,000 has been divided amongst the Adventurers, and a large sum laid out in the Machinery and Materials on the Mine. It must not be supposed, however, that in realizing this large amount the Mine has been exhausted, on the contrary the deepest Level, only 180 fathoms, is the richest part, and the prospects of this invaluable Mine were never so bright as at present. The Ores of Copper and Tin are of the very richest description, as may be seen by reference to the account of Sales published in the Provincial Papers and Mining Journal, whilst the expense of raising them, when compared with other Mines in the County, is very small. A Dividend has been declared regularly, every Two Months, averaging about £1,100 per Month. A new and splendid Steam-Engine, of 40-inch Cylinder, has lately been erected, another excellent Draught Engine (not in use,) three Steam Whims, and all other necessary Machinery and Materials are on the Mine, so that as there will be no further outlay in Machinery for many years, the Dividends must necessarily increase. The Setts have been recently renewed for 21 years, at the very low Dues of 1-20th.

In about 1842 another claimant appeared to claim rights of all minerals raised from beyond the low water mark – the Duchy of Cornwall. At the time it was reported that "an unprincipled claim has recently been made by the Government, on account of the Duchy of Cornwall, to the right of minerals raised beyond low-water mark, under the bed of the sea, which, in whomsoever the right of the mineral there raised may be, can only be approached through the lands which abut on the sea; the claim, therefore, is grossly marked by injustice, oppression, and folly". However, the Duke of Cornwall held sway and the lords could only look on with chagrin whilst the boundless treasures of Levant were "brought to grass" on their property to the exclusive advantage of the owner of the foreshore, and the Crown.

Levant about 1840, showing the pumping engine and the general chaos at the surface of the mine. The engine house here is for the old pumping engine and the picture appears to show the erection of the new whim engine house. The shears over the engine shaft may have been used to help lift masonry for the new building.

Drawn and etched by A. M. Scobell of Poltair, Madron, Penzance

This very early view of Levant is taken from an engraving in the Royal Cornwall Museum, by kind permission of the Royal Institution of Cornwall.

Drawn and engraved by W. Willis, Penzance

By this time the mine had already acquired its reputation as a tough place to work; in the Children's Employment Commission's report of 1842 it was stated that "In Levant they work six-hour cores (shifts). The mine is hot and deep, and it is considered that six hours will work a man down" The cores worked were forenoon (6am-noon), afternoon (noon-6pm), first core by night (6pm-midnight) and last core by night (midnight-6am).

Between 1834 and 1842 the mine produced 21,374 tons of copper ore, yielding £255,538, as well as large quantities of tin. Profits during this period had exceeded £150,000. J. S. Courtney's *Guide to Penzance* (1845) gave a description of Levant, stating:

Almost every thing belonging to this mine has a reddish colour, not only the ores, but the heaps of rubbish are red; the skin also of the men on ascending from their labours seems dyed with it, and the sea is coloured by the red water to some distance. There are machines here for draining the mine of water, for drawing up the ores and the rubbish, for crushing the copper ore, and for an operation called jigging; and at a little distance are stamping mills worked by water for pulverising the tin ore. The copper ore is the vitreous or grey sulphuret, some of it extremely rich, containing from 40 to 50 per cent of pure copper. The lowest level is now 240 fathoms below the surface. Levant was worked at least two or three times before the present adventurers commenced their operations; this last attempt has been one of the most successful in Cornwall; the fortunate proprietors never expended above £500, and they have gained in this time upwards of £135,000.

In 1845 five shafts were in use; the cost of sinking shafts in the soft ground around the lodes was £7 per fathom, but in hard ground away from the lode this rose to £30 per fathom. In February this year a woman called Grace Trembath, one of the bal maidens, was badly injured while working at the stamps. Accidents involving women were rarely reported, possibly they rarely happened, and this is the only one known for Levant.

In January 1849 a miner called Rosewarne was killed. He had been filling kibbles at the 130 fathom level; however when a kibble came up empty some of the men at surface went to look for him. His candle was found on the floor of the 130 but Rosewarne was found at the bottom of the shaft, having fallen 90 fathoms. A minor hiatus for the mine came later in the year over the failure of Messrs. John Batten & Son, the Penzance bankers and smelters. At this time John Batten was joint purser, and was obliged to resign. At a special meeting of the adventurers held on November 19th at the Union Hotel, Penzance, it was agreed that Lewis Charles Daubuz should act for the shareholders, and that the Batten family should forego dividends until the debt of 12s in the pound had been paid; Batten's offer was to pay his debt to Levant in installments of 6s in three months and 3s each in six and twelve months. Meanwhile, up to £500 was to be advanced to them in anticipation of dividends, a very generous offer. John Batten was also an adventurer in Wheal Owles, Boswedden, Wheal Reeth and Ding Dong, and was known as "The King of St Just".

Accounts published during 1849 show just how much money Levant was providing for its adventurers. In April a dividend of £12 was issued, leaving £1,100 in the hands of the purser. In June another £12 per share dividend was issued (£1,180 remaining with the purser) and another £5 in August (for May and June). This account showed:

Balance from last account	£1,172	11	4
Ores sold, less dues	5,437	9	4
Carriage and leavings	61	5	11
Total	6,671	6	7
Costs, coals and merchants' bills	£4,570	1	2
Rates and taxes	66	11	7
Dividend of £5 per share	800	0	0
Total	5,436	12	9
Balance in favour of adventurers	£1,234	13	10

Great days indeed!

Chapter 3

The Late 19th Century: 1851-1871 and an Early Closure

The year 1850 saw the mine acquire another engine, this one of 32 inches diameter, for stamping the increasing amounts of tin ore that the mine was raising. As before, it came from Harvey & Co., of Hayle. The following year the mine was being worked 240 fathoms "below the sea level" (*i.e.* 265 fathoms from surface) and a considerable way out from shore, "so that in rough weather the breaking of the waves upon the beach is distinctively heard by the labourers."

During 1853 the mine only divided £320 amongst the shareholders, against £4,000 in 1850. Sales of tin were now twice that of copper. On August 27th that year a very pessimistic report was published, regretting that the mine showed "symptoms of working out". However, while the mine had been producing large quantities of tin and copper for some years, it was not yet exhausted, as future events were to show. A labour force of 600 men, boys and girls was then employed. It was from about this time that the cost of those working underground, in getting to and from their places of work, was beginning to tell. Apart from the heat, there was a climb of 240 fathoms—1,440 feet—each day from the bottom of the mine, to say nothing of a fairly lengthy walk from the furthermost submarine ends back to the shaft before the ascent could even be begun. Something ignored by commentators of the day was the fact that men, boys and girls often had to walk several miles to get to and from the mine from their homes.

At a meeting on August 14th 1855, the adventurers made an historic decision, resolving "for the purpose of better developing the mine at the deepest levels, that a 'man-engine' be erected forthwith". Without this invaluable machine to carry the men to and from their labours the riches of Levant, lying at depths of up to a 100 fathoms and more beneath the then bottom of the mine, could never have been reached, and its career would inevitably have come to a premature end.

During the early nineteenth century, as mines grew deeper and ladder-ways grew longer, it was realised that some mechanical means of raising and lowering men in the shaft was needed to alleviate the huge effort required. To overcome this obstacle, one of the Fox family of Falmouth in association with the Royal Cornwall Polytechnic Society, in 1834 offered a prize for the invention and erecting in a Cornish mine of a device to carry miners up and down shafts without the fatigue of ladder-climbing. Fox's motives were partly humanitarian, partly economic; for it had long been realised that the miners' output was being seriously reduced, owing to the time and effort consumed in ladder

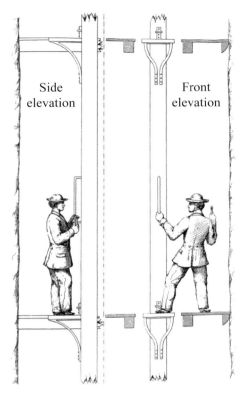

Side elevation

Front elevation

Layout of man-engine platforms at Dolcoath.

climbing. The award was gained by Michael Loam, and Tresavean Mine, in which his *man-engine* was first installed in 1842.

This appliance was of the same kind as the German *Fahrkunst,* comprising two wooden rods, with alternative reciprocal motion, to which wooden platforms were attached at 12' intervals. The miner stood on these, passing alternately from rod to rod in the shaft as the engine overhead made its repeated 12' strokes, bringing the opposing platforms momentarily parallel with each other. The Cornish man-engine was designed in a simpler form, with a single rod, the miner then stepping off on to a series of platforms or sollars fixed in the shaft itself a similar distance apart on each side of the rod, so that the ascending and descending men should not come in each other's way, each stream keeping to its own side of the rod.

The device was thus extremely simple, representing merely a specialised adaptation of the pitwork section of the Cornish beam pumping engine, then in use in nearly every mine. It could also be made to work in diagonal shafts, with the aid of rollers; the number of men which could be carried at any one time was considerable, this gave it a great advantage over any kind of winding gear then available for the purpose.

The man-engine proved an immediate success when introduced in Tresavean however its adoption by other mines in the county proceeded at a disappointingly slow pace. The reason for this was that in many cases the shafts were too crooked or narrow to be adaptable for the machine without the expenditure of a tremendous amount of capital, time and labour. In 1864, only eight man-engines were at work in Cornwall. The pioneer double-rod machine at Tresavean had by then disappeared but a similar one had been introduced at the United Mines; there were single-rod engines at Levant, Dolcoath, Cam Brea, Par Consols, Wheal Reeth, Fowey Consols, and Cook's Kitchen, the last two being driven by water wheels.

A report published on October 11th 1856, stated that the Engine Shaft was then about 230 fathoms under adit. About 17-18 tons of black tin were returned each month and 130 tons of copper ore, realising about £2,000, the cost being £1,900. The machinery then consisted of a 40" pumping engine; a 32" stamping engine, with 64 head of stamps; and two whim engines, one a 20″ and the other a 24″. Levant was now entering upon a period of renewed prosperity. In 1854 and 1855 dividends totalling £6 per share were distributed; in 1856 this was increased to £8 (£1,280); whilst by 1859 the annual distribution of profits had risen

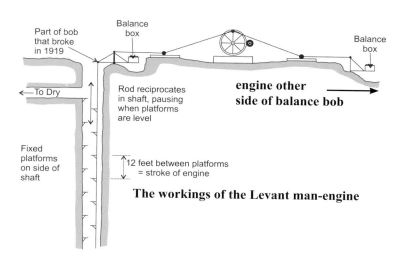

The workings of the Levant man-engine

to £3,200. The Levant man-engine was finally installed in 1857, working to a depth of 170 fathoms from surface. Motive power was supplied by a single-acting Cornish beam engine.

Throughout the 1850s Levant was one of the principal tin producers in Cornwall, though the mine's output was far from steady. At about this time Sir Warington W. Smyth began to compile a series of annual reports on the undersea Cornish mines for the Duchy office. This was primarily to keep an eye on the workings as they neared the coast, in order to note which mines owed dues to the Duchy. In his report for September 22nd 1860, he stated that a cross-cut at the 150 level had been advanced 60 fathoms beyond the North Lode without intersecting anything noticeable; it was itself on a cross-vein containing narrow ribands of brown jasper, with a little quartz and calcspar (calcite), but no useful mineral. The mine was in excellent condition for working, there being scarcely any accumulation of water in the deep levels under the sea. On September 3rd 1861, he reported the mine "somewhat improved in promise, if not in productiveness", the deeper levels, at 170, 190 and 210 fathoms on New Lode showing a tolerably good vein of ore, although in very hard rock.

On May 3rd 1862, Smyth gave the winding costs as £80 3s 4d per month, with no allowance being made for the sale of worn-out materials such as rope or iron. About 1,400 tons were drawn monthly at a cost of about 14d per ton. Winding was effected from Skip Shaft, with skips, from up to 245 fathoms; this shaft had both a southerly and northerly underlie, and included no less than four "corners".

Information on Levant was gathered by the Royal Commission appointed to enquire into the conditions of all mines in Great Britain, published as a Government "Blue Book" in 1864. The Commissioners conducted an enquiry in St Just on July 31st 1862, when Captain John Nankervis, described as being in charge of Levant, was questioned at some length. The mine then employed 70 men and 15 boys underground on tut-work. The

Engraving of Levant by W. Wills, Penzance, circa 1847. This shows an engine house on either Phillips or Zawn Brinny Shaft.

Used by kind permission of the Royal Institution of Cornwall.

greatest depth which had been reached was 245 fathoms. Several levels were "pretty warm", with temperatures of about 70° in one place. Copper was found there, and this mineral, rather than tin, was thought to produce these high readings.

The main problem at Levant was ventilation; because the main workings were under the sea the usual air shafts could not be sunk. Ventilation was therefore effected by driving two levels and sinking from one to the other. While this was being done, but before the connecting winzes could be completed, a "stool" was sometimes put in the back "to make a turn in the draught", while occasionally an "air machine" was used. The men judged when it was necessary to use such devices by experience and by being trained up to it. The boy who operated the air machine worked a shift of six to eight hours, a rota of three being required to cover the 24 hour period. Each pare of miners worked about six hours on piece-work, but a tribute-man could work 7, 8 or 9 hours if he chose. When the work was on tribute, the man would pay the boy for working the machine; but when piece-work was being done which had been set cheap, the mine provided the boy.

The captains visited levels in whose ends men were working perhaps on two or three successive days, or else two or three times a week, depending on individual circumstances. Should a captain find a level choked with deads, the miners were told "You must bring your stuff out, or we shall send people to bring it out for you, and keep the money from you to pay for it". The men sometimes allowed this rubbish to accumulate to such an extent that it impeded ventilation, and also restricted their efforts, "for when they are crammed up they cannot exert themselves with the same vigour". This was done to save the cost of removal. If they got a boy or other men to take it away, the removal would

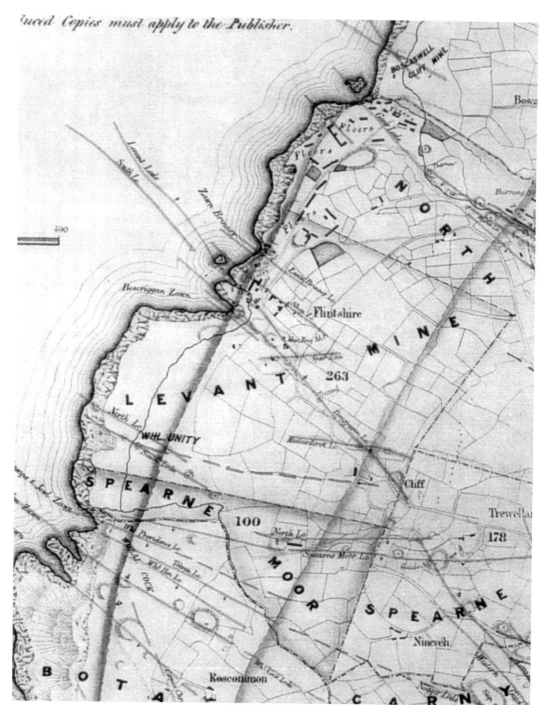

Part of Symons' 1857 map of the St Just mining district showing Levant and the surrounding mines.

only be effected once or twice a week, which was not often enough, and had to be guarded against.

The men paid the mine 9d a pound for their candles, which the mine probably paid less for. About two pounds per man per week was allowed, but larger amounts could be issued if they were working longer hours, or if any other unusual circumstances required it. For blasting, common powder was used. Asked if they had ever tried powder that produced less smoke, Captain Nankervis replied that a lighter powder had been tried, but no difference could be perceived. Deductions were made from the men's earnings for the club and the doctor. The club money was to provide for accidents, and amounted to sixpence per month. A similar amount went to the doctor, and covered attendance both for the miner himself and his family, except in case of fever, and for the services of the midwife.

Evidence from Alfred Chenhalls stated that a wire rope had been used for winding as an experiment; it had cost £500 but had altogether failed. Chenhalls thought this was due to the crooked shafts on the mine, the rope wearing out on the rollers. Levant was the only St Just mine which had tried wire ropes, though they were introduced at Botallack after the fatal accident in the Boscawen Diagonal Shaft in 1865. A flat hempen rope was used at Levant after the trial.

A large stone building served as a drying and changing house, the lower part being for drying purposes. The house was 70′ long and 14′ wide. It was well lighted, ventilated, and kept very clean. A continuous stream of warm water passed through the building, in which the men washed themselves. This dry replaced one burnt down in 1859.

In November 1863, Smyth reported that the 150 cross-cut had at last cut a new lode beyond North Lode, whose favourable appearance for rich copper ore had raised the adventurers' hopes. However, its position at the far end of the mine under sea, with difficult ventilation and in very hard rock, would make it a work of many months to explore it even for a few fathoms. Another cross-cut was being driven southward beyond South Lode and its branches at the 130, though this was also in hard rock. A year later he described the new lode at the 150 as exhibiting "a little excellent ore" which offered a favourable prospect for further exploration. A trial was being made on the Boscregan Lode, further south, which might ultimately be carried on under the sea. In October 1865 the Engine Shaft had reached 254 fathoms below adit; the tin ore here was promising and would be followed seawards.

In 1865 a total of 245 persons was employed (180 men, 17 females, 48 boys) representing a big drop on previous years. The lords were Mr Robyn's executors (one moiety), Messrs. Trezise and partners (the other land moiety), plus the Crown for the part under the sea. The depth was 254 fathoms under adit (30 fathoms). Minerals to the value of £16,428 17s 9d had been raised in 1864, but dividends were then in abeyance; only a small rise in the price of tin would ensure their resumption.

The first hint of impending trouble was given by Sir Warington Smyth in his report to the Duchy office dated November 16th 1866. After noting that a cross-cut southward at the 170 had failed to intersect the Boscregan Lode, he stated:

The dry. In the foreground is part of the railing around the staircase leading down to the tunnel connecting with the Man Engine Shaft.
Copyright Trounson-Bullen Collection

In May last, much excitement prevailed in the district in consequence of the alleged danger of certain workings recently opened up by the Managers, under the sea, above the 40 fathoms level. The men refused to go down the mine, and the Lords were applied to, to have the place inspected and reported on. Being in Cornwall at that time, I descended the mine for the purpose, and found, about 150 fathoms W. of the Engine Shaft, under the sea, that workings had been opened some 12 or 14 years ago to a height of 8 or 9 fathoms above the 40, and that a large stream of salt water was making its way down. Some good tin ore had tempted the Captains to resume these workings, but after what had occurred and on my objecting to their extending further, the excavations have been stopped at this place, and the strong timbering, with "stulls" and large cross-pieces, which has been put in in aid of what has been constructed some 12 years ago, will, I think, guard against accident. As to the water, I think that from recollections and what I learn from the captain, the influx has not really increased for some years past; and that the leak is therefore placed in strong rock throughout, and need not make its present appearance raise apprehensions.

Despite the danger of the "40 Backs", work at this level was not completely suspended and in 1867 some copper ore was discovered here, though this was not as extensive as had been expected. However, working for tin was entirely abandoned from fear of the sea breaking in. On November 17th 1868, Smyth recorded operations continuing on the Flat Lode at the 130 and 150 in an area between the Levant Old Lode and the North Lode, where enough tin had been discovered to give returns for some time to

In the foreground the tramway from the ore sorting area on the right. The tramway led to the stamps. Apart from the tall pumping engine house other buildings on the left are difficult to identify, except the explosives house in the distance.
Morrab House Library, Penzance

come. Little was doing on the North Lode itself, though a level was being opened on it both ways at the 220, and the 210 east had improved somewhat. At the bottom of the mine, the 264 level was driving on a small vein carrying a little tin, but pinched up between hard granite walls, apparently the only representative of great Levant Lode at this depth.

Meanwhile, relations between lords and adventurers had been steadily deteriorating; and on November 24th 1869, the *Cornish Telegraph* published a very gloomy account of the mine's position and prospects:

In the history of Cornish mining Levant has played, and we trust will yet play, a very important part. It is one of the oldest and deepest mines in Cornwall, and has, at divers times, maintained thousands of our mining population. In fact, it has been one of the principal agents in promoting the commercial prosperity of this district. We much regret to state that at present its affairs are in a precarious and uncertain state. During the past week the quarterly financial details have been issued to the end of June last, shewing for the three months an expenditure of £3,511 17s 9d. The credits are, tin and copper sales, and sundries, £3,158 6s 1d. This, deducted from expenditure on the quarter, shows a loss on the three months' working of £326 11s 8d. This lessens the balance due to the shareholders at the previous account to £485 5s.

But more anxiety is caused to the general public by the fact that it was resolved that "Inasmuch as it appears there is now little probability of terms being made for a renewal of the lease, it be an instruction to the purser and agents to prepare for winding up the concern at the time of the expiration of the lease".

This must certainly be regarded as a very critical state of affairs . . . The lords of the mine have, for a long time, complained of the manner in which the mine has been worked, and expressed their want of confidence in purser, agents, and all having the direction of affairs. They further state that, in their opinion, the workings of the mine have been carried on in a very restricted manner as far as the tutwork operations are concerned. They also allege, as a grave cause of complaint, that at the 40 fathom level West (under the sea) the excavations have been carried outwards and upwards to such close proximity to the sea as positively to endanger the safety of the mine, and thereby imperil the prosperity of the lords. Under these circumstances the lords have declined, thus far, to grant any new lease, "unless the mine is put into a proper state of repair, in accordance with the requirements of the reports made by our agents".

The committee offered to abide by the decision of two referees, an offer declined by the lords. Both Captain Joseph Vivian and Warington W. Smyth regarded the level as secure. On December 18th, Smyth notified the Duchy that he had had several interviews with the lessees, lessors, and Messrs. Rodd and Cornish to try to induce the parties to act amicably in arranging terms for a new lease, "but certain violent personal antipathies appear as yet to prevent any approximation". He had again inspected the 40 backs, accompanied by Captain Simmons, the Duchy's resident agent, and, contrary to what the *Telegraph* had reported of his conclusions, found the place to be in a very dangerous state. The lord's advisors believed the only way to ensure safety was by building a strong stone arch from end to end of these high backs; but Smyth believed this to be impracticable, as it would have to span a width of from 20 to 30 feet and perhaps even 40 feet, whilst the abutments would be very insecure, and probably require the cutting away of additional ground for placing them. For the present, the whole had been timbered with much care, and the agents were quite ready to put in "pieces" or props wherever it was suggested that more strength was needed.

Following the failure of the 1869 negotiations for a new lease, the "Old Company", as it later came to be called, continued to function. At the quarterly account held on the mine on March 24th 1870, the accounts for six months to the end of the previous December showed a further worsening of affairs, a total debit balance of £1,192 7s 2d having to be carried forward. At the meeting it was stated that the tin now on the mine was more than adequate to discharge the debt on the books. Mr. Borrow resigned his office as purser at Levant, which he has held for the past 20 years, and John C. Daubuz was appointed in his place.

By June 30th 1870, the debit balance had nearly halved to £667 3s, and it was reported that the 100 fathom level was driving at £5 per fathom for tin. In August the mine was employing 79 men and boys underground; men, boys and girls at surface, 97; total 176. The wage bill had dropped from £1,400 to £1,500 monthly in wages a few years earlier to an average of £600 to £700 monthly in 1869.

The final account meeting of the old Company took place in the Lecture Hall, Public Buildings, Penzance, on March 13th 1871, where a debit balance of £644 7s 9d was carried forward. The shareholders were told that the lords had refused to take the mine and materials at a valuation; they would not grant new setts without restrictions as to modes of working; and in short, no arrangement could be come to between them and the mine executive. Accordingly it was decided that the mine and materials be offered to the lords; on their non-acceptance the materials to be sold. "A mine that has been worked half-a-century, sold a million pounds' worth of ore, and given a quarter of a million in profits, is to be extinguished because lords and adventurers cannot agree".

Chapter 4

A New Year and a New Start

Proposals for a new company to work Levant appeared in May 1871; the cost-book company was to be in 5,000 shares at £3 each. The lords promised a 21-year lease, with 1/20th dues on copper and 1/24th on tin. The old plant was to be taken over at a valuation and made thoroughly efficient by repairs and additional machinery. It was reported that more than a quarter of the shares had been immediately taken up locally, mostly by merchants such as Messrs. Bolitho, Messrs. Coulson & Co., Messrs. Holman & Sons, J. Batten and G. Bazeley. The mining interest was represented by S. H. James, E. and H. Davy, Messrs. White and Messrs. York and Son. Other shareholders included Dr Richard Quick, Peter Olds and Dr Richard Searle, these three were to become notable characters, being particularly outspoken at meetings and in correspondence in the local papers.

The new company's first and most difficult task was that of putting all the equipment in good order. Captains Henry Boyns and James Thomas, the agents, reported in June that when they took possession of the mine on January 19th, both it and its machinery were a complete wreck. "Everything had been allowed to get into a ruinous condition; but a considerable amount of new work and repairs had already been effected, and a good deal of the wreckage cleared away. Underground, there was much activity in exploring new ground and prospecting the most promising portion of the old works.

One of the first tasks for the adventurers was that of replacing the old worn-out pumping engine. A new 45-inch cylinder machine was ordered from Messrs. Harvey & Co. of Hayle, and installed by Messrs. Eustice & Son, the engineers. It was first set to work on August 21st 1872, and on the 24th all the workmen who had been involved with its erection, between 50 and 60, sat down to a celebration dinner, presided over by Richard White. Captain Henry Boyns proposed "Success to the New Engine," and the "Health

Large group of miners on unknown level, date also unknown.

Looking up Boscregan Zawn at the pumping engine. From this angle all of the machinery appears to be on stilts. In the right foreground can be seen part of the miners' path down to the adit; the large crevice is most likely due to erosion along the weak rock around the lode.

of the workpeople of Levant Mine". By contrast, Wheal Busy, near Chacewater, celebrated the installation of two new pumping-engines with an ox-roast for all hands.

Also at about this time heavy repairs were made to the 33″ stamping engine, and the man-engine was overhauled. The labour force was increasing, nearly a hundred being employed underground, and about the same number at surface.

In December 1875 another accident happened on the man engine. A young man called Perrow was going underground on the machine but, apparently taking fright (it was only his second day on the mine), failed to stop at the right moment and fell onto the next lower step. Although he broke no bones he appears to have been crushed by one of the steps as "the pressure was so great as to seriously injure his bowels, and he lies in a very precarious state". A bell had formerly hung in the shaft to signal the engine-man, but this had not been replaced.

In June 1881 another boiler exploded at the stamps. The roof and one end of the boiler-house were completely destroyed, and slates and stones were hurled twenty or thirty yards away. Fortunately no injury occurred this time, either, but had the accident happened an hour later men would have been passing by on their way to the count house to be paid, and would probably have been injured by falling masonry. The man in charge had left the boiler house ten minutes previously, and the explosion was said to have surprised him as he was in the act of lathering his face for a clean shave!

In the early 1880s there was something of a scandal over the quality of coal being supplied to Levant, as the in-adventurer involved had picked out all the large lumps for himself before weighing off coal for the mine, and he was obliged to resign. The out-adventurers, by contrast, had to content themselves with the dividends (or calls) on their shares, and played no part in the management of the mine. Some of these were called "knife and fork adventurers". For the good liver of limited means it was worth buying just a single share in a prosperous company to enable him to wield a knife and fork at the account-house dinners which followed the periodical meetings. A stockbroker friend says this was sound investment practice, that of spreading the risk over a number of mines, and that this is still a basic tenet of investment theory. Knife and fork shareholders are not unknown to this day.

The principal shafts at this time were the pumping-engine shaft (known as Engine Shaft), Skip Shaft, and the Man-Engine Shaft, plus Guide Shaft to the south-east of the main workings at the part of the mine, near the boundary with Spearne Consols. The latter is known as Higher Bal. Other shafts were Phillip's, Unity, Boscregan, Angwin's, Tresize's, Goldsworthy's, Guide and Batten's. The first-named was so close to the base of the cliff that at one stage the sea broke in and the shaft was filled. Horse whims served the first two named and the plats survive.

Skip Shaft, whose earlier name, if it ever had one, has been lost, was used for hauling and was served by the hoisting or whim-engine. It was also very close to the cliff edge, and, curiously, only a matter of metres away from the pumping shaft. The two are adjacent to the whim-engine house and the ruins of the pumping-engine house. Levant, unlike many Cornish mines further inland, had no great water problem. Granite may be thought to be

View of Levant showing the boiler house for the whim cut down; at this time steam was being provided from the boilers for the pumping engine. The unlagged pipe can be seen just above the cut-down walls. A leat is in the foreground.

an impervious rock, but this is only true of the fine quality granite. In the whim-engine house it may be observed in the top chamber that the weather side wall is damp in winter, because the building is of inferior granite. When the engine was in steam, of course, the damp was kept at bay.

Fortunately, the main part of the mine's underground workings are under the sea and in the hard, impervious, greenstone. Consequently Levant, as well as the other St Just mines, was able to make do with a pumping-engine having the comparatively small cylinder diameter of 45 inches, whereas in mines further east they had 80-inch, 90-inch or even 100-inch cylinders. Again, the whim-engine is quite small, a 24-inch recylindered to a 27-inch. But it only had to lift one-ton skips of ore and not a great weight of counterbalanced pump rods. The downward skip was counterbalanced by the upward skip; as one rope on the drum paid out, the other rope would wind in, cancelling any effect of the rope weight.

In 1880 the first compressed air drill had appeared, with a Harvey compressor at the rear of the pumping-engine house. The first compressed air drills were extremely expensive (and very heavy) and their use was restricted to important areas of development. Though their advantages were obvious they were initially used on a very small scale, for in the St Just district the lodes are typically narrow as compared with tin and copper lodes in other parts of the county, and on very narrow lodes it was common (and easier) for a man to work single-handed with a borer if no country rock was to be removed.

February 1881 was a bad month for accidents. On the 14th a 22-year-old man named William Davey was killed while tramming at the 230 submarine level. When going to the front of the tram wagon in order to remove the pin before tipping, he lost his footing and fell between three and five fathoms, breaking his neck and dying shortly after he was brought to surface. The following day a man called Josiah Matthews fell on the tram road and caught his foot under one of the wagons, following which he had to be carried home. The day after an un-named man going down one of the shafts was hit by a falling stone which cut one of his hands severely.

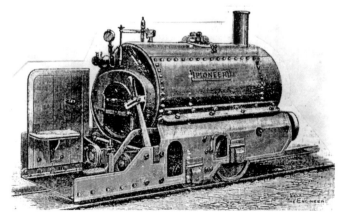

Levant's equipment in the 19th century was not restricted to fixed plant and power drills. In October 1891 the decision was taken to acquire a small steam-locomotive to tram underground. The 278 fathom level was the main tramming level of the mine, and it was thought that a small industrial **The locomotive unsuccessfully trialled at the 278 fathom level.**

One of the ponies on the 278 fathom level. The picture is posed as the ponies were only used for pulling empty waggons.

locomotive by Bickle of Plymouth could perform the job better than hand-tramming. The 278 was enlarged to 5ft by 5ft to take it. It was by no means a specialised machine which could consume its own smoke as existed up country. But the decision-makers would not have to put up with the heat and smoke.

The locomotive was a failure, however, partly because the slope in the level, which had not previously been considered for locomotive haulage, was too steep and partly because the wheel flanges also jammed on the rails in the 278. Just prior to this a pony had been acquired for tramming and more after the trial, the 278 subsequently being renamed the Pony Level. This was a sad admission of defeat in a county where Trevithick invented the steam locomotive, the "mobile power pack of the Industrial Revolution". In view of the difficulties of getting men and machinery under ground in Levant it may well be asked how the ponies fared. The answer was in a sling with legs tied together down the Skip Shaft. The RSPCA did not catch up with this.

In 1891 there was a strike over the serious matter of the quality of dynamite supplied. The miners preferred the German product to the British one which the mine supplied. It was admitted that supplies of the latter, which had been on the mine for twelve months, had deteriorated. In the same year there was a strike over the imposition of a time-keeping record. The men's spirit of independence rebelled against the idea of having their names taken as they went under ground. After a short time the management explained that it was only in the interests of safety and in cases of accident, and the recorder, a man known as "Dick Marker", otherwise Richard Grenfell, became an accepted institution (see photo overleaf).

In 1893 the beam engine working the man-engine was replaced by a horizontal tandem compound condensing engine, with a 5-foot stroke and cylinders of 18-inch and 30-inch diameter. The benefit of the man-engine to the miners and to the mine's production

Miners on the steps of the dry. Top right, Richard Grenfell, 'Dick Marker', who tallied men onto the man engine.

Jack Corin Collection.

may be expressed in the following terms. In mines with only ladder-ways the miner might climb upwards of 1,200 feet a day, and that labour alone would equal the maximum permitted in a prison treadmill and did not take into account the working of a shift. So while Dr Johnson, the great lexicographer (1709-84) might say that for a sailor "being in a ship is like being in jail, with the chance of being drowned", he could have made a similar comparison between a Cornish miner's life and that of a prisoner on a treadmill. Certainly climbing ladders promoted pulmonary diseases before the mining industry invented, in effect, silicosis. That was caused by inhaling the silica dust raised by the early waterless pneumatic drills.

At the Higher Bal section of the mine, some way up Levant Road, the 35-inch engine both pumped and hoisted; the latter function could be clutched in and out. The abandoned engine house is a fine example and the wall against the road, with its flight of granite steps and ore chutes, is impressive.

In the shafts sunk from the surface in Levant the engineers had a peculiarity to cope with, typical of older Cornish mines. The shafts were not vertical, as on modern mines, but followed the dip of the lode, which was neither vertical nor free of change. This was obviously an economical procedure when mining proceeded by the most laborious manner of hand-drilling. It was said that the Skip Shaft paid for itself when sunk. Nevertheless it suffered several changes of direction, and is a good example of what was known as a corkscrew shaft. Had the expense of swiping or straightening and enlarging it ever been undertaken the history of the mine's last few decades might have been vastly different. The shafts for the pumping-engine and the man-engine presented similar difficulties.

However, in 1895 Levant did in one respect march with the times, and installed telephones underground, only nineteen years after the Scottish emigrant Alexander Graham Bell perfected the first "articulated telephone". This was installed by Valentine Corin, AMIEE, of the Anchor Foundry, Penzance. In those days a foundry could supply all sorts of equipment, including a kitchen range, a bicycle, a lavatory cistern or gear wheels, all made on the premises. Remarkably enough the first mine in Cornwall to have underground telephones was West Wheal Eliza, near St Austell, which tried them out in 1877. With its neighbour Wheal Eliza, the mine was run by a Birmingham syndicate and had a go-ahead and highly skilled manager, Richard Harris Williams.

In order to minimise the costs of carrying materials to and from Penzance, Levant Mine had acquired a traction engine in 1883 with a second added in 1895. These appliances appear to have been a constant source of problems, not only tearing up the roads of the district but also managing to damage part of Falmouth Docks in 1906! To add insult to injury it was discovered in 1910 that one of the engines (the heavier) had been run without a license, causing a demand for tax arrears from the County Council. Other incidents involving the engines included the running down of its guide (and his subsequent death after losing both his legs) in 1898. In yet another incident, in 1908, one of the engines, pulling two wagons and 20 tons of coal, slewed off the road and hit the wall above the railway line opposite Lannoweth Road, Penzance, nearly falling onto the tracks. What the people of Penzance thought of these monsters as they rumbled through the streets

Count House Day at Levant c1895. Note the boys of school age.
Jack Corin collection.

with their trucks is not recorded.

The other St Just mines had no alternative to the horse and cart for taking mine produce to Penzance and bringing back machinery, as well as coal to feed the ever-hungry mine boilers. Somehow they contended with Trig-the-Wheel Hill, a long gradient on the St Just side of Newbridge, and this must have been something of a struggle even for the traction engines. Damage to the bridge here meant that it had to be re-built in the early 20th century with costs met by the local mines.

The shafts sunk from the surface were not the only ones in the mine. The submarine section, the most important one, eventually reached a depth of 350 fathoms below adit, and had two sub-vertical shafts, the Old and the New Submarine Shafts. The first was some 1,300ft to seaward and the second a similar distance beyond it. They connected the 210 and 302 fathom levels and the 260 and the 350 fathom levels respectively, and both were vertical. The Old Submarine Shaft was provided with a steam winding-engine and boiler in a man-made cavern. It worked despite the heat and smoke. In 1897 the New Submarine Shaft was provided with a compressed air winding-engine built in a large cavern carved out by the miners.

In 1898 a new form of power arrived, a 6 horse power Hornsby oil engine, replacing the water power used for the buddles and calciners. It was a big change from the four 20-foot water-wheels in use since 1842. In 1898 its man-engine was extended down to the 266 fathom level.

General view of the mine, date unknown. The tramway to the stamps can be seen to the rear, where it is elevated to reach the top of the stamps. The count house is on the right.

Visitors outside the count house. On the right, miners with bunches of candles. The figure in the dark suit and white jacket is, at a guess, Captain Ben Nicholas, a notable Levant character.

With more rock drills and a greater need for compressed air the management acquired a huge air compressor from Holman Brothers, the Camborne engineering company. To hold this monster a splendid new compressor house was built. Only a fragment of it remains, beside its very tall chimney with decorative bands and 1901 date stone. The new engine was a large horizontal triple-expansion model designed by George Eustice and Nicholas Trestrail. Its 18-foot diameter 20-ton flywheel must have been impressive in action. It supplied air to the drills under ground and also to the air hoist at New Submarine Shaft.

The christening ceremony for the new Levant compressor took place on 22 December 1901 and was reminiscent of those once reserved for the starting of some big Cornish pumping engine. To escape a typical wet and stormy day on the Pendeen cliffs, everybody crowded into the magnificent house where they were shown over the compressor by John and James Holman, Nicholas Trestrail and Mr Plummer, Holman's chief designer. Major Richard White gallantly offered the honour of starting her up to Major Frank Oats and the compressor 'went off as smoothly as a clock and was the subject of general admiration and satisfaction'. Toasts were drunk in Major White's special punch, who proposed 'Success to the Compressor'. Frank Oats was slightly overwhelmed by its sheer size and power, which was far more than was required at present and it was now up to the Levant agents to ensure they used its power to develop the mine.

John Holman claimed the compressor was faultless in every way, despite intense inspection by a bevy of engineers inside and out. James Holman was rather more lyrical, commenting 'a good compressor was like a good picture it needed a good frame and they had every reason to be pleased at the manner which the Levant company provided the frame'. He referred to the magnificent compressor house with its tiled floor and 100 foot ornate chimney with its Gothic concrete cupola. It was made from 2,000 tons of masonry which had cost a pound a ton, enraging many shareholders who resented this expensive 'elaborativeness'. Indeed, when Nicholas Trestrail submitted his bill for erecting the compressor, the Levant committee reduced it by £17 and dismissed him.

In August 1905 the *Mining Journal* printed a remarkable story about Levant Mine and its apparently lackadaisical attitude towards the transport of crude arsenic soot.

The big Holman compressor which caused so many disagreements on the mine.
The Trevithick Society

The Levant Mine has created quite a sensation at Redruth by sending crude arsenic loose in trucks, and dropping samples in the main or Fore street. It is an entirely novel way of advertising the well-known As_2O_3, and when Mr W. M. Martin, the leading chemist in the town, picked up a lump dropped outside his shop, and declared it sufficient to kill 150 people, the District Council thought it time to stir in the matter. The clerk was instructed to communicate with the Camborne and Redruth Urban District Councils, and there was some talk of action on the part of the police. It appears that the management at Levant have been invited to – for their own profit and the public safety – pack the stuff in barrels, but they have hitherto appeared to assume that crude arsenic is too cheap to pay for barrelling. There is a good deal of recognised waste in the Mining Division, but this is the first time attention has been called to loss in arsenic tailings. In the meanwhile the three candidates for Parliamentary honours might note the fact that, just at present, Camborne and Redruth districts are not precisely health resorts.

No further accounts were published in the press and it is presumed that Levant tightened up its arsenic handling procedures.

At surface a great variety of machinery not connected with the work of the shafts had accumulated over the years, in addition to the dressing plant. In the north-eastern part of the mine was the 32-inch stamping-engine. Only a small part of the house, with tiled floor, and its boiler chimney remains. In 1906 it was made double-acting and its power improved. By 1909 there was a battery of 96 heads of stamps, of which 76 were Cornish and 20 Californian.

The problem of hauling trucks up an incline from the vicinity of the Skip Shaft and bringing ore to the stamps was solved in a way typical of Cornish mining. A drive was taken for the winder off the end of the stamps drive. Cornish mining engineering was distinguished for three features, firstly brilliant innovation (as the career of Richard Trevithick shows), secondly ingenious improvisation, and thirdly (it must be admitted) what was known in Cornwall as a "lash-up", a phrase still in use to mean a dubious expedient. The print of Levant machinery in what must have been the days of the old company shows something like a lash-up in some of its features. The hard-worked stamps engine did yet a third duty; it pumped water from the adit for the processing plant.

In November 1909 an institution passed away. Major Richard White died at the age of 78, having remained vigorous to within two days of his death, and having attended a County Council meeting only a few days before that. He was born in Tregeseal, St Just, in 1831, but moved to Trewellard at the age of five and lived there for the rest of his life, looked after by his niece Miss White, for he was a bachelor. He had begun his service with Levant in 1850 as a clerk with the old company, and on its reorganisation in 1870 he acted first as secretary to the provisional committee arranging the formation of the new company and then as purser to the new company, steering it through good times and bad. The *Mining World* noted that he had been responsible for the equipment, which had enabled the mine to tide over the periods of depression. He always looked on the bright side, and his honourable and upright career commanded the support of all the adventurers. He was described after his death as the Uncrowned King of St Just; and it can be truthfully said of him that he *was* Levant.

Major White contrived to be purser of several small mines at various times, all situated

At the door of the count house: centre Major Richard White; on his left, Captain Nathan White (a brother) the Grass Cap'n, in charge of surface plant. On the Major's right, Valentine Corin, AMEE, rather less smartly dressed.

within an easy distance of Pendeen. He also became Chairman of the St Just Rural District Council, a County Councillor, and a JP, which cannot have left him much time to command the No. 1 Company of the 1st Volunteer Battalion of the Duke of Cornwall's Light Infantry.* His career was somewhat marred in 1893 by the great quarrel with Captain Henry Trezise, who had joined the company in 1862 as an agent and who had been mine manager in 1875-82 and 1891-93. Trezise had made considerable contributions to the revival of the mine, and after a row in the committee of management he was dismissed. So White remained supreme, a patriarchal and much-respected figure, recorded in the verses mentioned below:

> The First is dear old Major
> Who is beloved by all;
> He's Manager and Purser
> And rules both great and small.

He must have been a comparatively wealthy man, for he eventually owned one-eighth of the mine. He always appeared on the mine immaculate in top hat and frock coat, and photographs of him show that he was something of a "swell", with a silver snuff-box on a chain, and, no doubt, a gold watch-chain as well.

On his retirement in 1907 from active service on the mine he was presented with a silver-mounted liqueur set with a card case underneath, a fitting reminder of his care in making the celebrated count-house punch. At his funeral, and funerals remain a notable event in

*While Major White is known for his association with Levant, he was also involved in a number of other mines. He was purser of North Wheal Vor (1860), Spearne Consols (1864-74), North Levant (1884-1888) and Wheal Geevor (1893-1902), the latter becoming Geevor Tin Mines, Ltd; he was purser and manager of Pendeen Consols (1858-68) and the Garden Mine (1860). In addition he was on the management committee of Lelant Consols (1855).

the life of west Cornwall, hundreds of people assembled outside his residence and the blinds were drawn in all the houses and business premises on the way to Pendeen church.

A year after the Major's death there was labour trouble of a different kind. It was not militant strife but the effect of men voting with their feet against the low wage rates of the mine. They were emigrating in numbers to foreign mining fields and taking their mining skills with them. It reached the stage where the importation of foreign miners was suggested, though this did not come to pass at Levant, only at Geevor after the Second World War, when Poles and Italians joined the labour force.

The First World War brought another shortage of labour, with miners called up into the army and put on mining work of a highly destructive nature on the Western Front, that of laying huge explosive charges under the enemy lines. In 1917 real trouble flared. The men had joined the Dockers' Union, later to become the Transport & General Workers' Union. That the management at Levant reacted strongly to such a novel situation is not surprising. The union demanded higher wages and was prepared to accept arbitration by the Board of Trade. The Levant manager was instructed to meet the Union, make no concessions, and indicate that the mine's committee of management would not be dictated to, a situation all too familiar in more recent years in British industry. But it must

View from the north side of the engine houses. The ore picking sheds are at the rear and the tramway from Skip Shaft can be seen. In the foreground is the tramway to the stamps.
The Trevithick Society

Captain Francis (Frank) Oats.
Mrs Claire Leith Collection

be remarked that back in 1906 Levant had actually introduced something like a modern profit-sharing scheme. The men as a whole body were to be given a sum equivalent to one-tenth of each dividend paid, as a bonus. Unfortunately the idea did not last beyond two payments, and was considered a failure.

In February 1918 the mine refused the union's demands for an increase in wages and a minimum wage rate. At the same time the shortage of labour persisted, a situation which normally leads to an increase in wages. In July a management offer of a 10% increase in wages, but no minimum wage rate, was rejected by the union. A serious strike followed, accompanied by extreme militancy, so that the Chief Constable was asked for police protection at the mine. Violence was being threatened and intimidation carried out; protection was offered to men who wished to work and bonuses for those who would keep the pumps going.

In the same year Captain Frank Oats died and another great figure passed from the Cornish mining scene. Besides his quarter share in Levant he had also been a major shareholder and joint chairman of the Basset Mines in Carnkie, whose buildings remain virtually intact but roofless. The Oats family retained Frank's interest in Levant, and his son Colonel Francis Freathy Oats, who had served in the Royal Garrison Artillery, took matters in hand and threatened to close the mine. The threat brought a settlement of the dispute, but for the management it was something of a Pyrrhic victory. The final terms, though, were in a sense enlightened. They were 20% on earnings of £6 a month and under, 15% on £6 to £8 per month, and 10% on over £8. Even allowing for inflation a low wage level is revealed, remembering that these wages were per month. But it must be remarked that the variation of the percentage awards over the various wage brackets was much fairer than an across-the-board method of most present-day wage settlements, which benefit the highest earners most and the lowest earners least.

Chapter 5

1919 and Disaster

The summer of 1919 brought a re-run of the dispute. There was another rejected wage demand followed by a threat to close the mine. In July, in view of an impending coal strike, all surface machinery was stopped except the man-engine, whim-engine and pumping-engine. The previous strike had also led to the flooding of the lower levels, and the mine was obviously just staggering along. On October 20th of the same year the man-engine suffered a disastrous accident. Thirty-one men were killed, the second worst disaster in mining in Cornwall, eclipsed only by the 40 men who died in 1846 in the flooding of East Wheal Rose in Newlyn East by a sudden deluge. After the accident Levant entered into a period of terminal decline.

The death of 31 men and injury of many others affected the district deeply, and over seventy years later the memory lingers on. Surprisingly a considerable number of visitors coming to the whim-engine house have heard of the disaster and are interested to see a section of the man-engine rod and have its functioning explained. It was all too typical of Levant that it should still be operating a man-engine. The ride to the bottom of the shaft took half an hour, followed by a walk out under the sea, which could be a further mile. Such a loss of time added to the cost of distant undersea operations, already inflated by ore-handling costs, led to the consideration of straightening the

A rather inaccurate drawing of the man-engine surface plant.
Royal Institution of Cornwall

Photograph of what is almost certainly a group of visitors to the mine posing outside the building which formerly lay to the south of the count house.

Penlee House Museum.

Skip Shaft so that men could ride in it, but like other good ideas it came to nothing. Whether it could have served for hauling ore and men and sending town tools and timber is doubtful.

The man-engine had been the scene of accidents during its period of use, and four men had been killed at various times and a number of others injured. Boys were accompanied for their first three or four trips underground, after which they were on their own. Illumination in the shaft was by five-wicked candles called 'grassocks'. It would hardly have pleased the present-day Health and Safety Executive, but the management did not forbid visitors to the mine to ride the man-engine. One, writing of a visit in 1887, quite cheerfully rode it, remarking that it claimed a man occasionally. It very nearly claimed him through a little error in placing his foot. On returning to surface he met two ladies who had been offered a trip underground, but who wisely declined when they learned what would be involved.

A curious, though fatal, accident happened in January 1861. Captain Henry Tresize senior and Captain Nankervis had been looking at the underground workings with a friend. While ascending on the man engine, Tresize looked down to see how his friend was doing and was crushed to death by the descending rod step. This was the first recorded accident to the man engine and all the more ironic as Tresize had been instrumental in having the machine installed.

Apart from the occasional casualty the management was none too careful about the man-engine. When it was extended in 1888 no knocker or signalling line was provided, and the Inspector of Mines saw to it that two members of the committee, who were large shareholders, were sued. Events cast their shadow before them, for twenty years later there was a serious accident. Between fifty and a hundred miners of the forenoon shift were ascending to the surface when a length of the rod broke. Several men were thrown down the shaft. Others were severely shaken by the sudden drop. Stones and debris fell down the shaft, and it was with considerable difficulty that severely injured men were brought to the surface. The wildest rumours circulated concerning the extent of the accident, but the management seems to have been little roused by the incident.

The man-engine was not without safety devices. The rod had wings, or catch-pieces, with corresponding sills, stout pitch pine beams, in the shaft, so that when the rod was at the bottom of its stroke there was a small uniform space between wings and sills. In 1908 the wings and sills had presumably prevented the detached portion of the rod from falling very far, but even then there were several casualties. On the afternoon of October 20th, 1919, the safety devices failed in their function. A full shift of men was ascending, which would have weighed about 10 tons. However, the man-engine was probably balanced slightly heavy at no load, not at half load like a roped lift; it was essential to keep the rod in tension at all times to avoid buckling of the rod on the downward stroke.

Womenfolk assembled near the Count House on the second day of the man engine disaster in October 1919.
Courtesy Royal Institution of Cornwall.

Experienced men noticed a strange vibration in the machine and those fortunate enough to arrive at surface very soon noticed that they had not been followed. Someone went to look along the connecting tunnel to the shaft and found that the engine had gone. The rod had parted from the beam. One man was seen standing on the first sollar and quickly rescued, but too bemused to give any information. But it was all too apparent that the rod had parted from the beam at the surface. It had happened near the top of the upward stroke. There were no sollars or ladders left. The rescue parties had to make their way down the cliff to enter the mine by the adit.

In falling the rod got out of line, missing the upper sills and catches and destroying others, and broke in two at 60 fathoms below the cap, so that the upper part, with thirty men on it, fell 46 fathoms to the 70 fathom level, destroying platforms as it went. This caused most of the casualties. The scenes of carnage were something which those involved remembered until their dying day.

Geevor Mine sent men to aid the rescuers. Two men could not be released for twelve hours. With a third man it took 48 hours to bring him out, but he died shortly after. The last body was brought out five days after the accident, a testimony to the enormous difficulties encountered by the rescue teams. The whim was used to bring some of the bodies to surface. When the bell on the adjacent building was tolled, the womenfolk or loved ones would come forward and try to identify the dead.

Back in 1970 under the heading Yesterday's Witness BBC2 transmitted a programme on the disaster, when eyewitnesses could still be found. Even in cold print it takes little imagination to envisage the horrors so graphically described, especially if one has ever been underground. In 45 minutes, mainly through the interviews with witnesses, the programme touched on most aspects of the case. Even looking back half a century the speakers had the eloquence of their generation. One is tempted to include the whole transcript as an appendix but quotes from some of the more dramatic passages must suffice. One of the first rescuers was William Angwin, who went down the ladder road:-

The ladders was swingin' forth and back, I found it very dangerous. A moan came from a man in front of me and there was a little piece of ladder there. I made to grip the ladder to save myself 'cause it shook me. I was bunch of nerves, believe me, and there he was with all the slush and everything running from the shaft, right down his face and mouth, and he was pinned by his right hand and knee to the wall of the shaft one side, and the left hand outstretched and jammed that side. He started to moan and groan again so, what I done, was put some timber there to ... took away the water that was runnin' in his face, and he was feeling very ... like he wasn't ... closed up then, went quiet so I guessed that I'd done something for him. Poor fellow he was picked up 'bout 5 o'clock in the mornin' ... He died later.

Albert Dymond said:

And I had a mate, he was there for a day and a half to two days and when he came out — seen 'un day or two afterwards, 'Well, what it was like, boy?' 'Well,' he said, 'it was like 'ell — a mass of fire with the iron and the wood and the stones all comin' down', he said, 'a mass of fire'. An' he was there for a day, day and a half standin' on this 2ft platform or step holdin' on to that. No light. He could'n move 'cause he didn't know whether he'd go down farther or not. He was there 'til someone fetched him out.

The newspapers carried stories of rescue and escape. Willie Lawry, a bright young lad, had started underground only about three weeks before and had a very narrow escape. He said:

I was two steps above it what we call the 80, that's 80 fathom. I was two steps above that when the engine broke away and I was dug out two steps below that — a matter of 48ft. Now the man that I worked with, he was a step above me and he was found down 110, and the man that was below me, a man called Willie Walters, he was dug out before they found me, and he was dead. So actually I was very, very fortunate. I had 36 stitches in my face and neck, lost all my front teeth, a collar broke, and eight ribs crushed. But — took me 12 months before I started to work again.

Men waiting at Skip Shaft after the accident. Engine Shaft is on the right.

LEVANT MINE DISASTER,

MONDAY, OCTOBER 20th, 1919.

A POEM

And the Names and Addresses of

31 MINERS

WHO LOST THEIR LIVES.

This leaflet was sold locally for 2d in aid of the Levant Disaster fund. For many years the identity of K. A. the author of the verses was unknown but in 2009 the 90th anniversary of the Disaster, he was identified as Kirby Atkins, a printer's compositor from Penzance.

Lines on the Disaster.

St. Just, Pendeen, and Neighbourhood
   Will never forget the day
When thirty-one poor Miners
   Were suddenly called away.

This fearful accident occurred,
   On Monday at Levant,
And many a home is fatherless
   Through this terrible event.

The Man Engine was at fault, they say;
   Whilst bearing human freight,
Though very near the surface, smashed—
   And sent them to their fate.

The awful strenuous hours that passed,
   Whilst bringing up the dead
And rescuing the wounded,
   The thought we almost dread.

There were many willing helpers
   Came over from Geevor Mine,
To help the rescuing parties,
   Which was merciful and kind.

The Doctors, too, must have our thanks
   For attentiveness and skill,
In succouring wounded comrades
   Brought to surface very ill.

The Parson and the Minister
   Both rendered yeoman aid,
To alleviate the sufferers,
   Christian diligence displayed.

Now in conclusion let me say
   To rich as well as poor—
Remember the Widows and Orphans
   Of those that's gone before.

K. A

Names and Addresses of the Miners who lost their lives.

Henry Andrews, Nancherrow Terrace, St Just.
John T. Angwin, Regent Terrace, St. Just.
Peter Branwell, Chapel Street, St. Just.
Thomas Branwell, Carnyorth.
S. J. Brewer, Church Square, St. Just.
George H. Eddy, Bosorne Road, St. Just.
John Ellis, South Place, St. Just.
William Henry Ellis, Chapel Street, St. Just.
W. J George, Cresswell Terrace.
John Grenfell, Cresswell Terrace.
William J. Harvey, Boscaswell.
Ben Hocking, Kelynack Moor, St. Just.
W. J. Hocking, Truthwall.
John Kevern, Carn View Terrace, Pendeen.
James Maddern, Carn Bosavern.
Matthew E. Matthews, Bojewyan.
Nicholas J. Matthews, Chapel Street, St. Just.
William J. Murley, Tregeseal, St. Just.
Matthew Newton, Carn Bosavern.
James H. Oats, South Place, St. Just.
Sampson Osborne, Chapel Road, St. Just.
Eddy F. Pascoe, Prince's Street, St. Just.
Tom Rowe, Cresswell Terrace.
Leonard Semmens, Nancherrow Terrace, St. Just.
Nicholas H. Thomas, Boscaswell.
John Tonkin, Boscean.
Edwin T. Trathen, Bojewyan.
William Henry Tregear Bosorne Road, St. Just.
J. Vingoe Trembath, Bojewyan.
William E. Waters, Chapel Street, St. Just.
John Wearne, Bosorne Fields, St. Just.

John James said:

> We was stretcher bearers, you know, has to take 'em back, found two down where I was doing in 50 level, one down and one up the next stage. We brought they two back, in there 'bout hour and half we was, then we got sent from there up 60 level, went up there and brought three or four back, dead. Then we's sent from there up 24 level and I think I, without tellin' a lie, I think we carried twelve back from there that night. I was afternoon shift. I went down 2 o'clock and never went home no more till 8 o'clock next evenin' and 'bout 12 we carried out there and two of them was our neighbours here. Yes, funerals here, funerals there, for days and days and days.

For those unfamiliar with Cornish parlance it should be noted that Albert Dymond, above, addressed his mate as 'boy'. This form of address bears no relation to the age of the person addressed! In fact it used to be said 'There are no men in Cornwall, only boys!' A young son would be known as *e.g.* Boy Harry. 'Boy' is now out of favour with a younger generation.

Bad news travels fast, so it is usually said. But on this occasion it was slow to reach St Just, only two miles away. There would have been few telephones in the area. Indeed, it may be thought remarkable that Levant, slow to embrace change, had one, until it is remembered that the mine had underground telephones in 1895. It was only when Levant's private mail bag failed to arrive at St Just Post Office that a phone call was made to the mine (connected to the public system at Penzance in 1912) by the Postmaster, Joe Williams. He spoke to George Polgreen, the Secretary of Levant, and later the Vicar of St Blazey for 33 years, having taken Holy Orders. To the enquiry of what the trouble was, Polgreen replied, "Don't ask me Joe. God knows what's happened over here yet." Perhaps the task of visiting those bereaved by the disaster caused George Polgreen to turn to God.

An official inquiry was held by an Inspector of Mines. The whole subject was very thoroughly examined in great detail. The conclusion of the cause of the failure of the engine was very simple. The rod was attached to the beam at the top by two strap plates, in the shape of an elongated U. It had been annealed three years before, but a close inspection when it was hot had failed to reveal a flaw in its manufacture which led to the eventual breakage. A melancholy reminder can be seen in the broken strap at which is in the reconstructed boiler house at the Levant Whim.

The Inquest Jury's verdict was "accidental death". Such a disaster would no doubt bring more legal consequences today. A fund was set up for the dependants of the dead men. The last living link with the disaster was Mrs. Anita Murley, "Granny Murley" as she was affectionately known in the district. She died in September 1985 at the age of 93. When her husband was killed she had two children and a third was born on the Boxing Day after. She lived on a small pension from the Disaster Fund and earlier in her life took

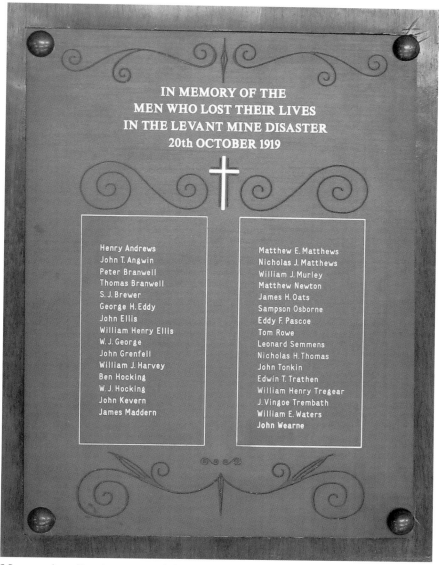

IN MEMORY OF THE
MEN WHO LOST THEIR LIVES
IN THE LEVANT MINE DISASTER
20th OCTOBER 1919

Henry Andrews
John T. Angwin
Peter Branwell
Thomas Branwell
S. J. Brewer
George H. Eddy
John Ellis
William Henry Ellis
W. J. George
John Grenfell
William J. Harvey
Ben Hocking
W. J. Hocking
John Kevern
James Maddern

Matthew E. Matthews
Nicholas J. Matthews
William J. Murley
Matthew Newton
James H. Oats
Sampson Osborne
Eddy F. Pascoe
Tom Rowe
Leonard Semmens
Nicholas H. Thomas
John Tonkin
Edwin T. Trathen
William Henry Tregear
J. Vingoe Trembath
William E. Waters
John Wearne

Man-engine disaster memorial plaque formerly at Trewellard Chapel and now at the Hard Rock Museum, Geevor.

Photo: Pendeen Community Heritage

in washing to supplement it. Three years before Mrs. Murley's death subscriptions were raised from private individuals and a memorial tablet listing the names of those killed in the disaster was placed in Trewellard Chapel at the top of Levant Road. It was duly unveiled by The Viscount Falmouth, Lord Lieutenant of the County. On the closure of Trewellard Chapel the memorial tablet was removed to Geevor Mine, where it can now be seen in the Hard Rock Museum of Cornish Mining. This fine museum contains much of interest about Levant and mining around St Just.

After 1919 the Holman compressor was replaced by a Belliss & Morcom 750 cu.ft./min. air compressor. At about the same time two 170-kilowatt steam electric generators were installed. It was the sort of plant which had almost become standard equipment on the larger Cornish mines during the so-called electric pump boom of the 1900s, and involved a considerable outlay; it probably represents the mines first and only attempt at modernisation. The power station at Hayle had been built as far back as 1906, mainly to supply Hayle and the towns and mines of Camborne and Redruth. It may appear to have been a wrong decision of the management to have installed its own generating plant but the decision seemed sound at the time as there had been no promise of a reliable public supply. In fact, the same decision had been taken at Botallack Mine after its reopening in 1906, the power station being taken out of commission in 1911, after the mains power supply reached the mine.

Chapter 6

Another New Beginning

An almost immediate result of the disaster was that at long last the only surviving cost-book company admitted it needed new capital. It had no reserves under its antiquated system of book-keeping and the result was that, just before Christmas 1919, shareholders were informed that agreement had been reached with Geevor. A new limited company was to be formed to take over the working of Levant, with an authorised capital of £160,000 in 10s shares, of which 40,000 would be allotted to the existing shareholders in Levant in exchange for their shares, 200,000 would be allotted to Geevor for cash, and 80,000 would be held in reserve. The new company, Levant Tin Mines Ltd., was registered in February 1920 in 320,000 10s shares. The board of the company was headed by Oliver Wethered, chairman of Geevor, assisted by Colonel Francis Freathy Oats, Lieutenant-Colonel Giles Oats (his brother), and J. Vivian Thomas, a solicitor. In 1925 St John Winne, a director of Geevor, and Professor James Gunson Lawn, CBE, joined the board. Lawn was an eminent mining man who, among other things, had written the standard work on mine accounting as early as 1897 while Colonel Oats had trained as a mining engineer at the Freiberg School of Mines in Germany.

In May 1920 90,000 shares were offered *pro rata* at par to Geevor shareholders, and by agreement 62,500 shares, credited as fully paid were allotted to Geevor, the total representing 52% of the company's capital. Until February 1922 a further 80,000 shares were under option in case the company needed further capital, but the option was never exercised. Shareholders in the liquidated company, besides receiving shares in the limited one, received 16s 9d cash per share, of which 9d per share was deducted and paid to the West Cornwall Infirmary. The adventurers must have felt

Levant's last manager Lieutenant-Colonel Francis Freathy Oats, eldest son of Frank Oats. Educated at the Freiberg School of Mines, he later became Deputy Lord Lieutenant of Cornwall.

Mrs Claire Leith.

The Californian stamps battery. On the left is the extension of the tramway past the Cornish stamps; the timberwork seen here is the chutes that passed the ore down to the stamps; the stamps themselves were in the timber structure which steps out below the ore chutes.

Russel Bayles

that they owed the hospital something, for in 1883 they resolved to contribute two guineas a year to it.

In the meantime there was the pressing problem of working the mine without the man-engine. Operations were suspended after the accident and were not resumed until the formation of the limited company. The captains suggested clearing the Man-Engine Shaft and putting in a gig, with a new winding engine. If only the Skip Shaft had been straightened as suggested in 1895, at least a temporary solution for winding men could have been achieved. A third of the men's time was lost in going to and coming from the submarine section, implying a loss of £6,000 a year. But when the cost was estimated at £30,000 the adventurers rejected the idea. It is said that Frank Oats then offered to sink the shaft at his own expense, if he could have all the ore met with on the way. It would have been a fair gamble, as the shaft would not by definition, have followed the lode down. Oats then caused some lavish expenditure on the mine, which gave a false feeling of prosperity and gave pay to men who might otherwise have gone to the Madron workhouse. That institution maintained a dismal way of life for the destitute, until the arrival of the Welfare State.

It was finally decided to sink a new vertical shaft. The site for it was chosen some distance east of the compressor house. Here a patch of level ground can be seen, covered with heather, where the ground had been cleared to sink the shaft. But no further work took place, and the heather spread over the ground, where the soil composition had been changed. A winding-engine bought from the Basset Mines, Carnkie, presumably a result of Freathy Oats' association with that mine, was never erected or put to use.

In the absence of a new shaft there was little choice of a way into the mine. There was no point in using the ladder road of the pumping-engine shaft, and the alternative was to go down the cliff into the narrow cleft of Levant Zawn and to enter the mine by the adit. The visitor peering into the zawn from a point near the whim-engine house may consider the choice as one of two evils. The new company inherited a vast amount of antiquated and worn-out equipment, and Thomas Robins Bolitho blamed the mineral lords for this. There had certainly been years of negotiations for a new lease, and until it was secured the company had been reluctant to incur capital expenditure. The mine had the misfortune to have three sets of mineral lords. One was concerned with mineral rights below the land (originally Messrs. Robyns, Trezise and partners) while the Duchy of Cornwall held the rights to the part between high and low water. Below low water the third party was the Crown, in the shape of the Office of Woods and Forests. The last-named described themselves as "lords of the undersea leases of South Trewellard Mine", but nowadays it is the Crown Estates Commissioners with whom companies like Levant must deal. The adventurers in both cost-book companies had cause for grievance in that one of the lords had formulated unreasonable terms for his lease, and was not prepared to discuss them. There was also the lords' insistence on the payment of royalties on mineral sales even when the mine was running at a loss.

In the end new leases were concluded when the limited company took over, but because of the deficiencies already noticed the company was obliged to abandon the submarine part of the mine, since men could not be expected to climb down to 350 fathoms or 2,100 feet, which would have rendered their labours uneconomic. The men did, however, climb down and up from the 190 fathom level below adit, or 1,140 feet. However, when they reached the mouth of the adit, with the climb up the cliff in all conditions of wind, rain and sea spray, they did not have a covered way to the dry. But despite the discomfort they were just glad to have a job.

Despite the abandonment of the submarine section, the working of the less-rich landward lodes, and the fall in the price of tin after the First World War, production of tin was quite good. Freathy Oats carried out development between the 130 and 190 fathom levels. It was remarked by another Bolitho, Horton, that Freathy Oats "lived for ten years on ground that had been abandoned in my grandfather's time". The mine staggered on against all the odds and its manifest deficiencies. As it was more recently said about a great surviving

Miners at Levant with candles stuck on their hardened felt hats with clay.

Jack Corin Collection

mine in Cornwall, it seemed to be a mine they could not kill, for all its century and more of ups and downs. But the end came in October 1930, in the depths of a world economic depression. The price of tin was dropping and had fallen to £99 per ton. A notice appeared in the dry stating that the mine would close the following Saturday. Of wages due a third would be paid following the sale of machinery and timber, a further third at the next Christmas and a final third the following Christmas.

Some years before this the Treasury had granted a £10,000 loan through the Trade Facilities Act Committee. As soon as the Company collapsed the Treasury appointed a liquidator and in the event all the plant on the mine, save the whim engine, was sold for scrap at the ridiculous sum of £600 and over 200 men had been thrown out of work. It took the heart out of the St Just mining district, where only Geevor remained to somehow survive. An institution had passed away.

The late Jack Trounson (President of the Trevithick Society 1981 to 1987) was then a young mining engineer, and engaged the interest of Josiah Paull, a director of South Crofty. Captain W. H. Ellis, the mine's former underground agent, compiled a report. Perhaps the most interesting part of the report is that he favoured an inclined shaft. (Such a shaft ultimately came to pass, but of that more later.) The incline would follow the richer values in the killas further westward, following the main ore shoot, save a great amount in tramming and provide better ventilation in a hot mine. Such was the temperature that it was said that it took three men to do two men's work. There would be a great saving in time in getting men to work and it was envisaged that the shaft would go down to a 400 fathom level. Captain Ellis reckoned it would more than offset the extra cost of sinking, extra hoisting power and higher maintenance costs.

Josiah Paull opined that the mine would make an excellent prospect in better times, but Jack Trounson's efforts to find backers were in the worst of times and, lacking contact with the City's capital markets, were unfortunately unsuccessful. Nevertheless, a few years later Jack was one of a small team of enthusiasts who saved the whim-engine from destruction and laid the foundations of the Trevithick Society.

However the time had not quite come to write FINIS to the Levant story.

Chapter 7

A Brief Reopening

Immediately after closure the machinery on the mine was coated in a black bitumastic paint, presumably so that it could be re-used if the mine was to re-open if the price of tin rose. It was the threat to scrap the whim engine in 1935 which caused the formation of the Cornish Engines Preservation Committee. In 1948 the Society became a charity, called the Cornish Engines Preservation Society. In 1971 this Society merged with the newly formed Cornish Water Wheels Preservation Society to form the Trevithick Society. From 1984 a group of Trevithick Society volunteers, which became known as the Greasy Gang, started working to restore the engine to its former glory and to make it run on steam. The old, worn-out, equipment was largely scrapped, but the more modern equipment was sold to other mines. The pumping engine was scrapped; during the process of removing the beam it stuck and had to be dynamited to encourage it out of the house.

Levant had been closed, or "knacked" (knocked) as they say in Cornwall. Even so, it was not uncommon for an abandoned mine to be reopened by an optimistic company. But Levant inherited a dire legacy from the former management - the so-called Forty Backs. This term was a byword for a weak spot in the roof (back) of the 40 fathom level. The trouble went right back to the days of Captain Henry Boyns, who, when he retired as manager in 1875, took the mine's section of the Forty Backs home with him, and it was not reunited with the other sections of the mine (then at Geevor) until some ninety

The recalcitrant beam of the 45-inch pumping engine, seen through the 'plug door' at the front of the engine house.

years later. In the level the miners could hear boulders rolling backward and forward on the sea bed when a heavy sea was running. Boulders is not an exaggeration: the sea is capable of moving rocks the size of a room in an ordinary house. In 1866, when Captain James Evans, of North Pool Mine, Chacewater, was manager, Warington W. Smyth reported to the Duchy of Cornwall Office that sea water was coming in the Forty Backs. Further excavation was stopped and additional timber supports were put in. This action seems to have taken place following two refusals of the men to go into the mine, such was their concern.

Derelict Levant seen from the sea, circa 1961.

In 1869 the old company was in disagreement with the lords over the Forty Backs. Captain Joseph Vivian of Reskadinnick, an eminent mining engineer at the top of his profession, carried out a further inspection, with which Smyth agreed (at least, at first). The lords were concerned with the safety of the mine and their revenue, though the *Cornishman* newspaper remarked that "the safety of the men was apparently a minor consideration, not even worth mentioning." Perhaps the lords thought the safety of the men was implied.

There is often a lighter side to potential disasters, and this one was no exception. One pare of men in the 40 fathom level kept complaining to the captain of sea water which seeped in, but he would not accept that there was any. One of the pare was from Sennen, on the coast about six miles towards Land's End. On his long walk to the mine he collected some limpets and placed them on the flow of water. So the captain admitted its saline nature! (Perhaps the record walk to work was that of a miner who worked in one of the lower levels of Dolcoath and walked five miles there and five miles back, six days a week for forty years.).

To make the Forty Backs safe the lords' advisers suggested that a strong arch be built, but Smyth objected on technical grounds. Later Captain William ("Kimberly") James, a member of the committee of management in 1883-93 and from 1899 to 1916 manager of Basset Mines, who had started as a working miner in Levant and who had worked in the Backs, recommended something similar in bricks and cement. But Major White thought it would mean that the miners would be afraid to work in the mine while the building was proceeding. In the event the timbering put in lasted the life of the mine, but not long after its closure. It is known from Captain Freathy Oats' own testimony (in the Levant annual reports) that the run which endangered the Forty Backs took place "on the last night of 1927". It is interesting that although a run of ground took place, there was no major ingress of water for over another three years.

Levant Mine in 1954; the whim engine house locked and secured.

A slight error in surveying had been made in measuring the depth of the sea above the Backs. In the nineteenth century it was put at 6 or 6½ fathoms (48 to 51 feet). In the 1960s it was found to be 45 feet. It would not have been too difficult to indicate the place to take a sounding from the surface of the sea. A boat could have been found from Portheras Cove to the north-east and a series of soundings could have been taken with a simple lead line. Of course they could have found no indication of the state of the ground forming the roof of the Backs, but they had certainly miscalculated its thickness. The point is that the sea eventually broke in and the fact was confirmed when Geevor, having noticed that the water in Skip Shaft rose and fell with the tide, put fluorescein dye down the shaft. A few days later it coloured the sea around the breach.

When the ghost of the wicked Tregeagle was laid it was bound to the task of emptying the reputedly bottomless Dozmary Pool on Bodmin Moor, with the aid of a limpet shell with a hole in the bottom. Dewatering Levant without completely sealing the sea breach would have been reminiscent of Tregeagle's labours. So Geevor, having already decided that its ore reserves were not sufficient without expanding its operations into Levant and developing that mine in depth, resolved as a first step to seal the breach.

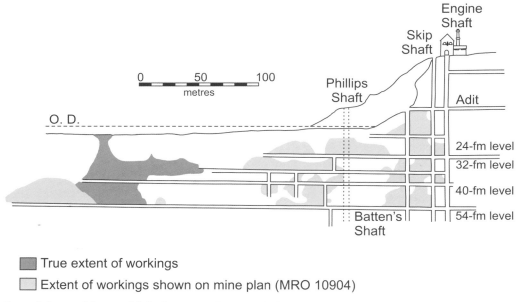

True extent of workings

Extent of workings shown on mine plan (MRO 10904)

One of the problems which the men who sealed the Levant breach had to contend with: the difference between the mine plan and reality.

The first attempt to seal the breach in the sea bed was made in 1961, when divers placed a concrete plug in the hole and put a reinforced concrete mat over it. But unknown to the engineers there was a wide gunnis with unstable walls and roof below the hole, where the lode had been taken away, and the action of the sea soon broke up the concrete mat. There was then a long pause for thought, for it was clear that the cost of sealing the breach would be high. As many of Levant's miners had put their labour and skills into developing the mineral wealth of South Africa it was fitting that the Union Corporation of South Africa Ltd. agreed to join with Geevor in sealing the breach and to contribute three-fifths of the cost.

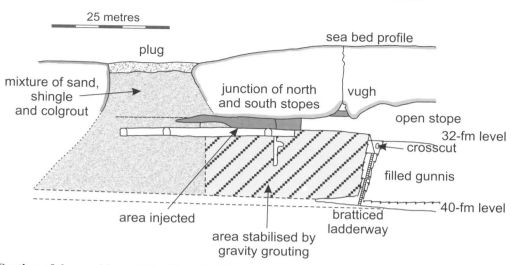

Ordnance Datum (Sea Level)

25 metres

sea bed profile

plug

mixture of sand, shingle and colgrout

junction of north and south stopes

vugh

open stope

32-fm level

crosscut

filled gunnis

area injected

area stabilised by gravity grouting

bratticed ladderway

40-fm level

Section of the workings at the 32 and 40 fathom levels showing the amount of ground sealed and grouted.

So in 1965 a second attempt was made to seal the breach. It began with pumping 30,000 gallons an hour of sea water out of Skip Shaft. This had the effect of drawing loose material from the sea bed into the mine to within a few feet of the bedrock, so that the bottom of the new plug would rest on natural fill. The remains of the old concrete mat were then removed, and a wall of sandbags filled with quick-setting cement was built round the hole for a good distance on either side of the breach. This gave the divers steady water in which to work, and successfully prevented the sea from causing any damage while the sealing was in progress. Conditions at sea were poor for most of the time, and the divers could only work about one day in three. They worked from a 35-foot ex-Admiralty motor vessel, renamed *Wheal Geevor*, in depths of water varying between 70 and 55 feet. Some 7,000 bags of quick-setting cement were dumped over the side to make a much larger new reinforced concrete mat. Then pipes were installed, leading from cement mixers set up on the top of the cliff and down into the hole. Volunteers from among Geevor's surface workers ensured that a constant supply of quick-setting grouting ran down through the pipes, night and day, for nearly a fortnight. About six hundred tons of concrete were laid under the sea in this way before the breach was filled. As far as is known no comparable feat in terms of distance, depth and location had ever been accomplished before. The technical achievement was remarkable, and won for its projectors the coveted Gold Fields award, the first time it had been awarded outside South Africa.

Life in connection with *Wheal Geevor*, 22 miles from her Newlyn base, was not without incident, although there were no casualties. On July 1st she struck the Vyneck Rock off Cape Cornwall through a combination of steering trouble, swell and low water and

sprang a serious leak. She was escorted into Newlyn by the Sennen Cove Lifeboat *Susan Ashley*.* On October 8th in the same year the weather turned very bad, and those on the cliffs wondered whether she would reach safety, and it took three hours steaming to reach Newlyn.

The concrete plug at the end of the 40 fathom level. This photograph of the concrete plug filling at the end of the level was taken in 1977, under fraught conditions: high humidity, water streams from the back of the level, over 6 inches of slimes and everything coated with mud. *Photo courtesy Bryan Earl.*

On one occasion a diver had the feeling that he was being followed and turned to find himself being eyed by *Cetorhinus Maximus*, 18ft in length and weighing several tons. The basking shark is harmless but the fear was that a flick of its tail might sever the air line and the decision was taken to kill it.

Following the success of the sealing, the mine was unwatered, a winding-engine was erected, and Skip Shaft was fitted out with a cage for the transport of men and materials. As each narrow level was unwatered men crept along them — there was just room to crouch — and put out a set of timbers. The sealing was not quite perfect at this stage, and sea-water continued to trickle into the workings. As each set of timbers was put in, the miner, working on his own, would tack an opened-out plastic fertiliser bag to the roof and walls so that he had a dry place to work in. One miner the author met told him he liked this sort of job, because it was a job with a challenge, and that he had gone round the neighbouring farms one Sunday to buy plastic bags at sixpence apiece. Once the timbers were secured the miners shovelled out the debris from under the concrete plug until there was sufficient space to complete the sealing and securing of the roof from within the mine. The work was finished by March 1966, and in 1967 diamond drilling was started in the old workings, including a horizontal hole from the 40 fathom level in the direction of Botallack.

At the 1979 Annual General Meeting the Chairman of Geevor was able to announce

*The *Susan Ashley* is now preserved and on display at Chatham Historic Dockyard. The *Wheal Geevor* was less fortunate; she sank on 21 October 1981 and now lies in over 60m of water 33km SSW of the coast south of Waterford, Eire.

that the sub-incline shaft from Geevor to Levant had been completed, that Levant would be tapped and drained down to Geevor's 19th level, with a drive from Geevor's 18th, to connect with Levant's 278 fathom main tramming level. (Geevor's level depths are measured in feet, thus the 18th level is at 1800 feet from surface. Levant's measures were fathoms below adit level.). It was also revealed that £2 million would be spent on developing and extending the mill. Unfortunately, once the opportunity had come to properly explore the old Levant workings it was realised that the expected reserves were not there.

So the career of the old champion Cornish mine had come effectively to an end. Levant was distinguished by its submarine development a mile under the sea, and for many features, perhaps not always for the best. It produced in its life a wealth of copper and tin and even a little gold and silver. If the management over a hundred and ten years had not always been as far-sighted as it might have been at least it was remarkable for its tenacity. The miners, over many generations, worked in very demanding conditions, subject to many hazards, but, like Raymond Harry, were proud to be miners working in the famous Levant. It bred characters as diverse as Dr Quick and Major Dick White. It had its terrible man-engine disaster, which even after ninety-five years (in 2014) is still remembered in the district and seems to have been implanted in the minds of many visitors.

Levant under the auspices of Geevor. This photograph dates from the late 1960s-early 1970s and shows the newly constructed buildings in white. The headframe has been erected and the pumping engine stack demolished. The patch of white material below the compressor house suggests the demolition of some of the new buildings.

The end for the story of Levant? In a sense it is not quite the end. There remains the winding engine, saved from the scrapman in 1935, and Levant's subsequent history as a tourist destination.

Chapter 8

Mineral procesing: the dressing of tin and copper ores

Tin Dressing Processes

The dressing of tin, that is preparing it for sale to the smelter, required several processes although the sequence was quite simple. This description will also be kept simple as there are relevant remains on the dressing floor. It should also be noted that tin dressing varied slightly from mine to mine as the nature of the cassiterite, SnO_2, the principal ore of tin, differed.

Tin ore was blasted from the lode underground and a certain amount of sorting carried out, particularly of the rocks containing no ore, the 'deads'. Any large pieces of ore were broken underground by hand, then all the ore was trammed to the hoisting shaft and brought to the surface. Once here it required fine crushing in order to go through the various processes. Crushing took place at the stamps; initially these stamps were water-powered, and later steam-powered; 'Californian' stamps were often electrically driven (a

The Cornish stamps at Levant; 32 heads can be seen on the right-hand side. At the far right is a bevel gear which was used to wind wagons up the tramway from Skip Shaft.

set of these stamps can be seen at King Edward Mine, to the south of Camborne). Water power was often limited to four to eight heads, whereas steam power could drive up to more than two hundred at a time (as at Dolcoath Mine, at Camborne).

The stamps reduced the ore to sand; during the stamping process the ore was mixed with water and it was as a pulp that the ore was moved around the dressing floors in a series of leats and timber launders. After stamping the pulp was fed to a series of convex, circular buddles. The material was delivered to the centre - the head - of the buddle and allowed to flow outwards from the centre. The tin concentrate, being about three times the density of the waste rock, remained near the head, with less dense material further from the head; rotating arms carrying brushes helped keep an even surface of material in the buddle. When the buddle was full surplus water was allowed to drain away before the buddle content was sampled. Some

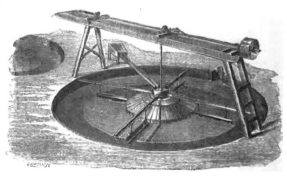

Drawing of a convex buddle.

material, the tailings, could be thrown away and other material, the heads, could be sent to the calciners (see below). The intermediate material, the middlings, needed to be reground before going back to the buddles and the process repeated. In the 20th century much of this process was replaced by shaking tables coupled with froth flotation; these methods of tin dressing can be seen at the Geevor Tin Mine Museum and King Edward Mine.

The very fine slime containing some tin oxide went into settling pits, where after settling

it was dug out, then concentrated on 'rag frames' and concave buddles. Using the techniques available until the early 20th century, and the difficulty of catching very fine particles, there was a limit to the amount of fine tin that could be recovered.

The partially concentrated tin ore was sent to the calciners. The job of the calciner was to roast the tin ore, converting the various and unwanted sulphides of copper, **Shaking table at King Edward Mine. This table had recently been used and the fan of material across the surface can be seen. The dark band on the left of the grey material is the tin concentrate.**

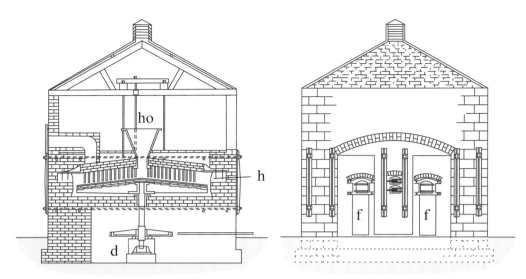

Drawings of a Brunton calciner: section left and elevation right.
d: calciner drive, f: fire boxes, h: hearth, ho: filler hopper

iron and arsenic to oxides and the sulphur to sulphur dioxide gas, which was drawn through a flue system and up the stack. Arsenic trioxide (at times a valuable by-product) was deposited in the flues. Where large quantities of arsenopyrite (FeAsS) were present, arsenic trioxide was collected in a long series of flues known locally in Cornwall as a 'lambreth', from the word labyrinth.

The Brunton calciner had a very gently sloping circular cast-iron plate onto which tin concentrate was dropped at its centre. The plate turned at a few revolutions per hour

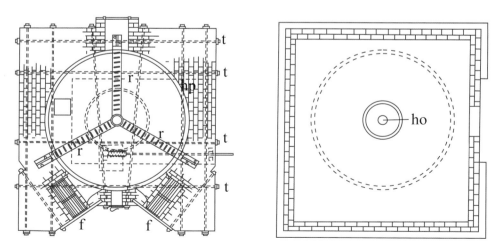

Drawings of a Brunton calciner: horizontal section left and top floor plan right.
f: fire boxes, hp: hearth plate, ho: filler hopper, r: rabble arms, t: tie bars

and the ore was raked, or rabbled, by three arms attached to the roof of the very shallow hearth in which the plate was located. Two fire boxes supplied hot gases which roasted the ore at a low red heat, converting the sulphides to oxides; this was a continuous process, unlike the flat-bed furnaces used on other mines. The temperature at the top centre of the plate was about 1100°F (600°C) while nearer the edge it dropped to about 1000°F (550°C). Most mines had roasting facilities of some sort, though some were only used for roasting the ore without the collection of arsenic oxide. This treatment removed awkward impurities and greatly helped the final cleaning of the tin concentrate up to top quality.

After roasting, the ore was again buddled or put across shaking tables and/or round frames for further concentration. Kieves were also used in the final cleaning; this process involved putting the concentrate into a deep wooden tub with water to make a thick slurry. The tub was then given a repeated knock on the side, and the effect of this was to make the denser material sink and the less dense (or poorer) to rise, so the latter could be skimmed off after all the material had settled in the tub.

Settling pits were used to catch fine material, known as slimes. In these pits the slimes would settle to the bottom and thicken, allowing clean water to be drawn off the top and recycled. The slimes could then be put through careful treatment in the mill to recover any tin.

Tin ore concentrate was sold to the smelter, either by ticketing, an open process where the smelter and the price were specified, or by private contract. The latter was common where a local smelter, who was frequently also a banker, held a large share in the mine. This was the case at Levant, where the Bolitho family, of the Chyandour Smelting Works and Mounts Bay Commercial Bank, had considerable influence.

Copper Dressing Processes

By comparison with tin dressing copper dressing was much simpler (because the ore did not have to be brought to such a high grade) and usually involved breaking the ore into smaller pieces, and many women and children picking and sorting the better ones. In many cases the ore was washed and screened ("riddled") and then "jigged" on a sieve to recover very small copper ore particles. Sometimes, lumps of ore were carefully cracked with small hammers to remove any waste material. The idea was to produce the equivalents of heads and tails (good and poor ore), and the terms "crop" and "halvans" were used, respectively. These processes included "spalling" (with heavy hammers) and "cobbing" (with small hammers). The work was carried out

'Bal maidens' spalling copper ore.

on a cobbled surface known as a spalling floor; the remains of one of which can be seen at Botallack Mine. Unfortunately for the workers these operations were often carried out mostly in the open, regardless of the weather.

Cobbing copper ore from a hand-barrow.

In later years the ore crushing became more mechanised, and on larger mines the 'Cornish rolls' crusher was introduced to crush the ore mechanically between cast-iron rollers. It is reputed to have been devised by John Taylor at Crowndale mine, near Tavistock, in 1809, though a patent for crushing material by metallic rollers had been taken out over 50 years before this. In its earliest and simplest form it was two counter-rotating lengths of cast-iron piping powered by a waterwheel or a small engine. These roller crushers (the cause of several nasty accidents) were often worked by a rotative beam engine, one of which was installed on the old copper floors at Botallack Mine to the south; a few fragments of this remain, including the engine bedstone.

Finally, the sorted copper ore was divided into piles of several tons each, which were inspected by the agents of the various copper companies who would then put in bids for them. There is some evidence of collusion by agents to 'arrange' the prices offered to the mine, in order to keep them artificially low.

The equipment used for dressing copper ore (as well as lead) was in the main constructed of timber. As a result of opportunistic reclaiming and recycling of these materials, it is often impossible to locate the sites of the dressing equipment.

Chapter 9

The Workers

Most historians of mines or groups of mines in Cornwall tend to concentrate on geology, engineering, or economic history. Little attention has paid by them to the men who did the work, or the women and girls on the surface, let alone the boys who toiled above and below ground from an early age. The great exception is the late Dr A. K. Hamilton Jenkin, whose classic *The Cornish Miner* was published in 1927 and subsequently reprinted several times. He covered almost every aspect of the miner's life from early times, and had the advantage of knowing men who had worked in the previous century. But even he said little about the female workers, the bal-maidens, as they were called, and we have to rely on essayists like George Henderson or outsiders like J. R. Leifchild. Other occasional travellers in Cornwall have added their comments, not least the Portuguese Alphonse Esquiros and a Manchester clergyman, Reverend F. J. Horsefield. The latter stayed at Pendeen vicarage a century ago. He visited Levant and observed the local scene.

He was a very keen observer and must have made very careful notes on his visit to the mine, for he describes what he saw in some detail.

Cornish miners were not apt to write their autobiographies, although some wrote verses and Thomas Merritt, an Illogan miner, composed tunes for carols which are still sung in Cornwall with enthusiasm. Levant had no composers, but an excellent writer in the late Raymond Harry of Carnyorth. In 1917 he went to

Study of a Cornish miner by Bennetts. Seated next to a ladder he has a pick in his right hand, bunch of candles (known as 'dips') attached to his right breast and a roll of safety fuze on his belt. He is wearing a felt hat to which is attatched a candle.

work in Levant at the age of fourteen, and in 1962 he published a book called *The Mine under the Sea*, under the pen-name of Jack Penhale. His accounts of various phases of his life in Levant would shame many who leave school at sixteen today, and some of the incidents he records would horrify an Inspector of Mines. He details working conditions in the mine in the twentieth century. We can be sure that they were as bad and worse in the previous century. For much of its life-span Levant had five or six hundred employees, men, women and children.

Apart from individual dangers there are three ever-present threats to health and safety in a mine, namely temperature, ventilation, and climbing ladders. The Trevithick Society party working on the restoration of the winding-engine was given an underground tour of Levant in October 1990. At that time Geevor was only running its upcast fan on a night tariff, so we may assume that the temperature of up to 82°F which the party recorded would have been typical of the mine when it was working. The humidity was very high. One member of the party weighed himself before he left home and found after the four-hour trip that he had lost 7 lbs. This was the same as the weight loss of a miner on a Levant shift, and he was probably ill-nourished by present standards. One, Henry Maddern, recalled that the 326 and 314 were the hottest levels and "would fill your boots with sweat."

Allied to the subject of temperature was the matter of ventilation in the mine. The effects of blasting added to the problem, as did the use of the steam-engine in Old Submarine Shaft, to say nothing of the underground locomotive. It has been questioned whether the smoke or "smeech" it produced led to its withdrawal rather than the slippery rails. Metalliferous mines are always more difficult to ventilate than coal mines with a more regular layout. In the case of Levant a large portion of the mine being under the sea compounded the difficulty. Under the land air-shafts could be used. Under the sea there were several answers. Winzes were sunk between the levels and stulls or screens were used to direct the draught from the air machines employed. The latter were fans turned by a wretched boy on a six to eight hour shift. Later, compressed air was sent down through pipes. The eventual solution, when the mine acquired large compressors, was to send compressed air down. This was applied in the 326, known as "Little Hell". It was said that there was hardly enough air there to keep a candle alight, but that the lode was "rich as a Jew's box". Smoking twist would hardly have improved the atmosphere.

The danger of an accumulation of radon gas in a mine where ventilation is poor was not recognised until about the 1960s. But Cornish miners in the last century may not have lived long enough to be affected by its alleged carcinogenic qualities. There was little silicosis, because most of the mine was in the killas rather than in granite. But many Levant men went to the hot, dry mines of the Rand before water to keep down the dust was introduced into the drill shafts. They earned good money but shortened their lives.

Cornish miners suffered more from pulmonary diseases through climbing ladders in shafts but the Levant miners were spared this by the introduction of the man-engine. They also had the benefit of a changing-house. One was burnt down in 1859, and the one which lasted until the mine closed was built in 1888. In 1899 it was joined by a flight of spiral stone steps to the head of the Man Engine Shaft via a tunnel. This meant that men coming up did not have to face the weather before they had changed into their outdoor clothes.

Workers on the surface, men, women and boys, had obviously a rather healthier life than the miners underground, but the distinction was only relative. Victorian writers tended to exaggerate the virtues of working in the open air. The workers were more hardy than present-day people, because they were used to the open air and had but little heating at home. Survivors of shipwrecks would live all night in conditions which would kill the average present-day human in an hour or less. The Reverend Horsefield wrote: "The floors on which the bal-maidens work are kept beautifully clean, and the work is performed in sweet pure air. The happiness of sunshine is around the people, and brightens their lives." In fact, fog is prevalent in the St Just-Pendeen area, and not only in winter. It has a micro-climate which can produce persistent fog in summer when the sun is shining only a mile or two away. It is said that the people of St Just never minded working underground because they never saw the sun anyway!

The Trevithick Society workers on the restoration of the whim engine at Levant will testify to the incidence of rain, wind and fog. In the winter, when it was not one of the three, it was often all three together. The surface workers at Levant must often have had their own thoughts about working in the "sweet pure air", since waterproof clothing was hardly known to them.

For those on the surface there were dangers from the machinery, but at least they could see them. For the men underground there were always hidden dangers, not only those concealed in rock which might fall. The standard **Two miners stoping the back (roof) of a level on a rather precarious platform.**

illumination was by a tallow candle. The miners wore hard felt hats and on them were stuck the candles in a lump of clay. There could hardly have been a cruder method. Even the illumination from a modern miner's electric lamp seems to the layman underground only just adequate, and it is hard to imagine how one coped by the light of a candle. It was not until 1927 that Levant progressed to carbide lamps, which had been introduced in other Cornish mines over twenty years earlier.

Group of miners stoping at East Pool Mine. Note that there are two miners near the top of the photograph, in the background. The only time that these men would have seen the size of the cavity they had made was on the rare occasion they were visted by a photographer. Note also the large hole at the bottom of the image, crossed by a timber plank

The present-day preoccupation with health and safety at work was seldom shared by nineteenth century employers, even though a mine's General Articles, which included rudimentary safety precautions, were read out to the miners at regular intervals. Blasting was a particular hazard, using quills or reeds filled with black powder for a fuse. In 1831 John Solomon Bickford invented the safety fuse, a great gift to miners all over the world. Until then the sight of a maimed or blind miner, hurt in a blasting accident, was all too common in the mining districts of Cornwall. Indeed, in St Just it may have continued longer, for in the 1920s the late A. K. H. Jenkin met miners in west Cornwall who had used black powder throughout their working lives. Herbert Thomas, a noted mining journalist a century ago, cheerfully remarked that "dynamite either kills or does not hurt." Levant men raised to an art the biting of the cap on the detonator to secure it to the end of the fuse. A slight error in this process, instead of using the special pliers provided, would have led to death.

It is a sad fact that no county hospital existed (in Truro) until 1799, having taken five years to build. Cornwall's second hospital began its life ten years later in Penzance. Commencing in 1809, the Penzance Public Dispensary and Humane Society was set up near the Market House in Market Jew Street, and in 1813 moved to Chapel Street. In 1871 the Dispensary acquired part of the old poor house (*i.e.* the work house) at

St. Clare, with a view to opening an in-patients section with beds. The West Cornwall Infirmary and Dispensary finally opened on August 13th 1872 not officially in use as such until January 1874. The first Miners' Hospital was built 1836; it was just outside Redruth at West End and has been redeveloped.

It is not known when mines began to employ their own doctors, but the system appears to have been in operation by the middle 1700s. A few pennies per month (known as 'doctors' pence') entitled the men (and sometimes their families, as at Botallack Mine) to free medical treatment from the mine's doctor. In some instances this also included the services of a midwife. Unfortunately small mines could usually only employ one doctor, who would not necessarily be popular with the men he attended. Only on larger mines could this particular problem be avoided. An additional problem on small mines was that an appointed doctor might not always be on the site. Doctors' pence was finally abolished with the introduction of the Metalliferous Mines Bill of 1872, at which time the amount paid had gone up to 1s a month for men and 6d a month for boys and girls. This would pay out £1 and 10s per month respectively for sickness. Unfortunately money for the 'sick club' was often included as an asset in the mines' accounts, and could be, and usually was, distributed among the adventurers as part of a final dividend on the closure of the mine.

A group of bal maidens and male surface workers at Dolcoath, circa 1900.

Mine doctors were not as a rule elected by the miners themselves, but usually by the managing committee and even occasionally by the mineral lords themselves, by a clause in the lease of the mine. This system was not popular with the miners, and potentially caused problems to the mine if the lords were involved as cases occurred where leases would not granted if particular surgeons were not employed. The strike of the St Just miners in April and May of 1853 was largely called to force the managers to allow them to choose their own surgeons and to put all sick club money into one account, rather than one for the doctors salary and one for sick pay - it was unsuccessful.

During his time as a young man in Levant in the first quarter of the century Raymond Harry describes a particularly dangerous maintenance job he and three others undertook at the end of the 278. They had to repair the launders there, from which water was leaking into the stopes below. It was known that the place was dangerous because of rotting timbers and loose heavy ground in imminent danger of collapse. On the way the danger signs were all too evident, and they negotiated a large hole spanned by an eight-inch wide plank with the help of the timber they were carrying with them. No Inspector of Mines would have allowed them to go on this trip: any loud noise or false step could have meant disaster. The return journey was even more hazardous as they had nothing with which to supplement the eight-inch plank. They arrived at the shaft in safety, pursued to within an inch of their lives by a cave-in or "run of ground" heard throughout the mine. Such was a day in the life of a Levant miner!

That was not the only alarming and out of the ordinary experience which Harry experienced when in Levant. On one occasion he and his workmate were asked to find where the rising main in the pumping engine shaft had burst somewhere above the 278. They set off up the ill-maintained ladders of the Engine Shaft, not even by the light of tallow candles, for they were doused by the water coming down. In the ascent they were in constant danger from the plunging pump rods, thin or missing rungs on the ladders, and slippery sollars at various stages. Only his workmate's splendid memory of the difficulties of the shaft saved Harry. After ascending a ladder which hangs slightly backwards they came to the 40 fathom level where the burst of the pipe had occurred, not, as the Captain on the surface thought, low down not far from the 278. Having made a temporary repair they ascended to the adit level and climbed 250 feet up the cliff path to meet the Captain in the pumping engine house. He was astonished at their feat in climbing the shaft so far in the face of a deluge of water. He accepted that the two men have had enough for one day and were going to change and go home!

Having survived the shift without mishap the Levant miner spent up to half an hour ascending the man-engine to the comforts of the dry. On emerging from it in his dry clothes he faced a walk home. That could be several miles, perhaps over rough cliff paths, pleasant enough for a summer stroll but not so in the dark of winter in the wind and rain. If we take as a random sample the unfortunate 31 men who died in the man engine disaster we find that 17 of them lived in St. Just, two miles away as the crow flies. By the

Three bal maidens filling a wagon at Carn Brea Mine. From *Harper's Magazine*, **1881.**

shortest road route it was three miles and there was no public transport, even if it could have been afforded. One wonders to what extent miners ever used bicycles.

Miners' pay was based on the price the mine received for its ores, standard prices for both copper and tin being notified to the men at the beginning of a contract. An early record was made in 1837 by Sir Charles Lemon for the Journal of the Statistical Society, which was reprinted in De la Beche's geological survey of 1839. The wage rates in mines west of Penzance were then the lowest in the county. Tributers received 47s 6d per month, tutworkers 45s and labourers 42s. Mine workers were paid on a four or five-week month and not a 52-week year. In June 1881, with a high tin standard, pay at Levant was the best for twenty years, with tributers receiving £5 4s 6d and tutworkers £3 18s 8d. Two years later, with a lower metal price, underground men were receiving £3 15s a month, boys £1 0s 2d, surface men £3 and surface boys 10s.

Individual tributers might have a good "sturt" or rich strike in one or two months; for instance, in 1874 two tributers on a two-month contract in the 210 cut a rich bunch of ore and received £40 each for eight weeks' work. But in general wages remained low; with a low tin standard the average at Levant in 1893 was £3 a month, never more than £4, while bal-maidens received 5s and girls 3s 6d a week. At about this time C. V. Thomas, the lawyer member of an eminent Camborne mining family, was moved to remark "When miners are paid better we can expect them to work fifty hours a week instead of thirty or thirty-five as at present." One can hardly believe he was speaking seriously!

By 1910 Levant men were earning £4 15s a month underground, and good men could earn £6 to £7 15s. In Raymond Harry's time pay had risen to £6 a month, compared to £100 to £120 on the Rand. It is worth remembering that as late as 1939 a labourer's wage in Penzance was only 30s a week. Because monthly wages were inconvenient for miners, it became the custom for pursers to make advances of pay or earnings weekly or fortnightly. These were known as subsist or "'sist", and were accounted for at the end of the contract, when the "taker" of each gang of men received an account and a cash payment of any balance due to him and his mates. Mine managements frequently charged for candles at a price slightly above those charged in the local shops, in order to discourage miners from selling them and taking unnecessary risks with insufficient light under ground. The cost of candles was charged to both tributers and tutworkers, as were pick hilts, tools, doctor and club, fuse, powder or dynamite, and the mine barber if there was one. Miners were "spaled" or fined for breaking mine regulations or for not completing their bargains, 2s 6d for the first offence and 5s for the second, a considerable sum in those days.

It may have come as a considerable shock to the committee of management of Levant when the Employers' Liability Act was passed in 1881, for it took the mine two years to implement it and to take out the required insurance against accidents involving miners. For many years the men had paid 6d. a month into a sick club, which covered accidents and medical attendance of the mine doctor, Dr Quick, and which extended to sickness at home.

The Education Act of 1870 introduced a basic improvement in the life of children, but it was two years before an Act was passed excluding boys under twelve years of age from working under ground, and limited children's working hours at surface to ten hours a day. In the middle of the nineteenth century there were the beginnings of a move to educate miners for their occupation. A great leader in this was Robert Hunt, F.R.S. (1807-1887), a notable figure in Cornwall. In the 1890s the district mining classes set up by the Miners' Association (of which he was secretary) were consolidated into the Camborne School of Mines, in a granite building in the centre of the town. Among

the institutions thus consolidated were the Redruth Mining School, the Camborne Mining School, the School of Arts and Science in Penzance, and the Penzance Mining School, near the Botallack count house, now a dwelling known at Botallack Vean. The Camborne School of Mines subsequently moved to Pool and is now located within the campus of the Combined Universities in Cornwall at Tremough, near Penryn.

Having made his way home with the aid of a candle in a treacle tin (if at night) and perhaps with the aid of his wife out looking for him with a lantern if he came over the cliffs; what sort of home did the man find? The many miners' cottages which survive in rows today look snug and

William James Rowe, the last driver of Levant's whim engine.
Trevithick Society Collection

big enough for two people by modern standards. A century and more ago they might only have had an earth floor and be likely to contain a family with several children or young men working at the mine. The bedrooms would have been crowded and the shift system making "hot bunking" a routine, now only spoken of in ocean racing yachts. (But well into this century railwaymen suffered the system in boarding houses of sleeping in a bed another man had vacated.).

Lighting, as used underground, was usually from tallow candles, although oil derived from pilchards was an alternative. Water supply was from wells in various locations about the parish, although many of these appear to have begun their lives as shafts - one can only wonder at the quality of the water. Mains water in West Penwith is definitely a twentieth-century invention. Sanitation was not an important consideration of the time, and diseases such as typhoid, diphtheria and scarlet fever took a constant toll.

The diet and quality of cooking depended much on the wife a miner had chosen. There was equal opportunity for women in the mining industry — as labourers. Many miners, not surprisingly, married bal maidens. These girls had little time, opportunity, or inclination for acquiring domestic skills, after a day spent breaking copper ore or dressing tin. And if mother had also been a bal maiden they had not the best of tutors. In any case a very limited budget dictated the diet and miners did not suffer from eating too much red meat. It was only seen for the majority on high days and holidays.

Despite the name the 'hungry forties' this was neither the first nor the last decade where food was scarce for the miner. In many areas little animal food (*i.e.* meat) was eaten, the diet comprising gruel and vegetables. A cup of tea, perhaps made from mugwort, and a piece of barley bread sent a miner to work, with a hoggan (a baked pastry containing currants or figs and sometimes a piece of pork) for his croust or mid-shift meal. On return his supper would perhaps be salt fish, tow rag (or toerag, dried salted cod), potatoes and mugwort tea. A night cap might be the cold comfort of barley bread, potatoes, and cold water. In such spare time as he had the miner could grow vegetables in his garden, keep a pig (if he could find sufficient to feed it), or even a cow or a half-share in one. Bread and pastry were usually made with barley as it was half the price of wheat, with wheaten loaves eaten on special occasions such as feasts and Christmas.

On the Cornish coastline any cove, or even wide cleft in the rocks was sufficient to keep a boat when hunger was the spur. Levant men were fortunate in having Portheras Cove, just beyond Pendeen Lighthouse, and Priest's Cove, under Cape Cornwall, from where they pursued fishing as a spare-time occupation. In the middle of the last century the former even attained the stage of holding a midsummer regatta for lug-sailed craft. Priest's Cove, with surrounding rocks and a swell coming in remains an awkward place to launch a boat. The tradition of part-time fishing was maintained by Geevor men to the end of that mine's life.

In the earlier days of Levant another source of additional income derived from the sea would have been smuggling, or 'Free Trade', as it was politely called in Cornwall. If the miner did not actually go to sea there was money to be earned in the transport of the goods on shore, and for the children to be told to "watch the wall, my darling while the gentlemen go by". This was not entirely poetic licence on the part of Kipling.

After the end of the Napoleonic wars the government was able to concentrate on the suppression of smuggling. If you look from Levant towards Pendeen Lighthouse (built 1900) there is a substantial row of white Coastguard cottages, with an observation tower at one end. It shows how seriously smuggling was taken in the district. The Coastguards' prime duty was not life-saving, as now, but maintaining an inshore blockade against the smugglers. To that end a boat was kept in Portheras Cove. We may be sure that not a few miners benefited from involvement in the Trade. To this day old people in West Cornwall refer to spirit beverages as a "drop a Trade".

The miners would also have derived windfalls of goods from the all too frequent wrecks of the nineteenth century. Everything from outright defiance to ingenious circumventions was practised against the Coastguards. It was permissible to salvage cargo as long as it was declared to the Coastguard. Needless to say declaration was made as little as possible. Old habits die hard. A few years ago a container of leaf tobacco came ashore at Pendeen. As a result it was said that the fog siren at Pendeen Watch was sounding not on account of a normal fog but because of a fog of tobacco smoke wafting upwards.

In October 1909 the mine itself was able to take part in salvage but necessarily on a legal basis. The *William Cory* came ashore under Boscaswell Cliff with a cargo of pit props. Levant agreed with the underwriters to salvage as much as possible of the cargo, the mine to receive 50% of its value.

Smuggling came to an end in the last quarter of the nineteenth century for a number of reasons. The blockade became more effective, there were changes in duties, more luxury goods, formerly smuggled, were produced at home and the game became less worth the effort, organisation and finance. Just as important was the influence of Methodism, for Wesley disapproved of smuggling as illegal.

It is no exaggeration to say that the brothers John and Charles Wesley transformed life in Cornwall, even in the remotest parts and among the poorest people. No other individual or organisation has had a greater influence on the spiritual, educational and cultural life of the Cornish people since the early Christian church. Before the coming of Methodism Cornwall might well have been called West Barbary, a name jokingly given to it in 1891 by L. L. Price which was taken from the title of a book published about North Africa in 1671. So poor and neglected were the tinners, miners, labourers and fishermen that they would descend on any wreck and dismantle it. Wreck timber, which was often of very good quality, occasionally found its way into mines to secure the workings.

From wicked rocks and shelving sands
From Breage and Germoe men's hands
Good Lord deliver us

As the sailors' prayer had it.

In practice low-church, Methodism civilised the county. Since the Prayer Book Rebellion of the sixteenth century and the resistance to the Reformation it implied, Cornwall has been either neglected by the Church of England or made the recipient of High Church parsons. The western parishes nevertheless maintained their patronal festivals or feasts, and they are celebrated by various events, both religious and lay. To this day, St Just Feast is still marked with considerable gusto!

At first John Wesley met with resistance in his indefatigable preaching. He was capable of delivering six sermons and riding over fifty miles in three days on one tour. When he began to make converts in Cornwall the people responded with enormous enthusiasm. Indeed, Methodism was known as Enthusiasm, but that was because in the eighteenth century the word meant "ill-regulated religious emotion or speculation". As such it was sternly resisted by many in the Church of England. A Bishop of Exeter, in whose Diocese Cornwall then lay, had inscribed on his tombstone 'A pious suppressor of Enthusiasm'; the famous Cornish historian, Reverend William Borlase, who held the living of St Just and Ludgvan in plurality, was a noted opponent of Methodism.

Methodism appealed to the enthusiasm, in the modern sense, of Celtic converts. Many of Charles Wesley's hymns remain firm favourites in the Church of England as well as the Methodist Churches. Song appealed greatly to the Cornish Celts, as it did in Wales. John Wesley himself said "Methodism was born in song" and nowhere was this more true than in Cornwall. The sound of voices filled not only the chapels but the pubs. Out of the chapels were born the male voice choirs, and the ladies' choirs, which are such a feature of present Cornish culture. The pilot gig racing clubs maintain the tradition regardless and can usually produce a soloist or two. Once upon a time the singers at the Tinners' Arms in Zennor were the finest singers and when Penzance Pirates XV beat Cardiff the Tinners' Arms men at Zennor beat the Welsh at singing that evening!

Church, Chapel or non-Churchgoers, Levant men had a singing tradition of their own. The shift coming off would sing during their half-hour ascent by the man-engine. In a BBC2 transmission in 1970 looking back to the man engine disaster a witness, Albert Dymond, described the singing. "They had four male voice choirs here in this district and most of the men worked in the mine and when they travelled the man engine they all started to sing and the sound that you heard as it came up through the shaft was out of this world. If you could stand on the top of that shaft and listen ... rich, it was, rich ... and some never used to believe in church and chapels or anything like that. Yet they would join in the hymns, you know, and everybody with heart and soul in it."

Charles Wesley.

On one occasion the shift coming to work in the afternoon told of a ship in peril off the Land's End, so the mariners' hymn Eternal Father strong to save was sung. The harmonies in the Man Engine Shaft must have been wonderful to hear. Sadly it was all over long before the day of the tape-recorder but what a recording it would have been!

The Non-Conformist lay members of the chapels had to manage their own affairs, without the help of an educated parson, and not least build their own Chapels. St Just has a vast Methodist chapel and there are other smaller chapels scattered around the district, built by miners and others with their own hands. Abandoned mine buildings were sometimes robbed for building stone for the chapels, something which a mining engineer once described as sacrilege! The chapels had their local preachers on the circuits, laymen who somehow acquired an education, but not always a perfect one. Many stories are told of their unconscious humour on occasions, such as the impromptu prayer which began "O Lord, as Thou hast no doubt read in The St Ives Times ..." One at least of Levant's captains, the manager, Captain Ben Nicholas (1871-1926), was a local preacher.

John Wesley.

A further benefit of Methodism was its emphasis on abstinence, though it did not make the Levant miners into teetotallers. Raymond Harry noted that on Maze Monday, the Monday after pay-day, half the men might be absent through the effects of drink. However, the Reverend Horsefall was able to report in 1893 that he had not seen anyone drunk in the course of ten weeks. Formerly pares of tributers adjourned to the pub to divide their earnings, and there was consequently much drinking, but by the middle of the nineteenth century many miners put their money into saving banks or bought small houses.

So little entertainment was provided that men could hardly be blamed for going to the pubs. The unfortunate bal-maidens were criticised for spending their little money on finery, bought from the packman, "Johnny-come-fortnight", a feature of Cornish life which survived into this century. After breaking copper ore all the week who could grudge them a little diversion?

It is hard to believe how little entertainment for people there was in a remote area like Pendeen-St Just. The wireless did not arrive until the 1930s and the cinema never came to St Just. Small wonder that annual events like Feast and Church and Chapel treats were looked forward to from one year to another. A visit to Penzance by the St Just horse-bus (traditionally "always room for one more"), if it could be afforded, was a considerable event. Travelling vans brought around domestic items for which there was no local shop and were too bulky to be carried on the bus.

Church or Chapel services, perhaps up to three on a Sunday for children, were an occasion for singing and perhaps a discreet eyeing of the girls. A typical special entertainment was reported by The Cornishman newspaper in March 1891.

> PENDEEN. An entertainment has been given in the Pendeen Board-schools by the Cripples Hill choir. Recitation &c were given by members of the Rechabite Society. The Vicar presided. A most enjoyable evening was spent by a goodly audience.

It was probably much better than most modern television programmes!

Foreign travel became popular but only in terms of emigration by the men to find employment in distant mining fields. A St Just girl asked by a stranger whether she had ever been to the Land's End replied, "Naw". The stranger was surprised, but his informant added, "a'course our people have been to South Africy and Australy". It was a St Just miner and a Scillonian who found the famous "Welcome Stranger" gold nugget in Victoria, Australia. It was the biggest single nugget ever discovered in the world, weighing over 200lbs and brought its finders John Deason and Richard Oates, the enormous sum of £9,500 (multiply by 32) more than they might have earned in a lifetime at Levant.

Chapter 10

The Levant Whim Engine

Introduction and History

As the 1840s approached the 20-inch engine which had been installed at Skip Shaft was at its limit and a revision of the hoisting capacity was necessary. The technology of the day pointed to a larger winder and a new headframe. The new winder installed in 1840 had a 24-inch diameter cylinder and a 4-foot stroke; it is was built by Harvey's Foundry at Hayle and designed by Francis Michell. It was double acting with a reduction gear from engine to drum of 3 to 1, that is three revolutions of the flywheel or driving gear would rotate the winding drum one revolution; this meant that a heavy load could be raised at a slow speed. The winding drums were small in diameter; the width between the flanges was narrow in comparison to their height above the drum because they were designed to accommodate a chain, these having been introduced in 1820. The half-inch diameter wrought iron type was in general use later with a safe working load of 1.6 tons and a breaking load 7.6 tons.

In 1843 development had reached the 220-fathom level (402m below sea-level). It is thought that the engine was running at about 48 strokes per minute, near its safe maximum, and the flywheel turning at 24 revolutions per minute. The weight of ore in the kibble would be something like 10 to 12 cwt. Therefore, in order to keep the mine in operation below 220 fathoms, a modified winder was needed. Modernisation at that time would take into account:

- chains to be superseded with an iron rope (was introduced from about 1850).
- a larger cylinder 27½ inch (0.69m) in diameter with a 4 ft. (1.2m) stroke.*
- a direct drive to the winding drum.
- probably a bigger flywheel.
- the shaft to be timbered for skip hoisting.

Calculations show the 1840 winding drums were big enough to take a 1-inch or 1⅛ inch diameter iron rope to 278 fathom (510m below sea-level).

During the 1860s the engine was damaged when the flywheel burst, possible through a rope breakage; the repairs were carried out by Hocking and Loam. At the time of the accident the engine was winding with a single drum and would have been using hemp rope. The damage was probably worse than realised and may have caused the breakage

*Re-cylindering may have taken place later: see opposite.

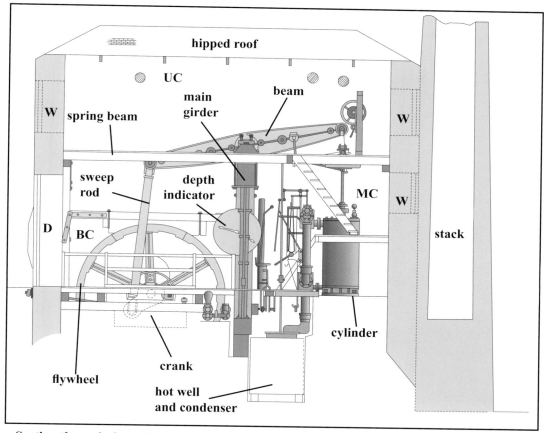

Section through the whim engine and engine house showing the main parts of both.
Redrawn from Courtney Rowe's *Drawings of the Levant Whim*.
BC = bottom chamber; MC = middle chamber; UC = upper chamber; W = window;
D = door

of the lintels under the cylinder, discovered during the millenium refurbishment (see below). The beam gudgeon was bent and the cylinder and piston were probably damaged and this may have caused the engine to be re-cylindered. Because of the recylindering the mounting position appears to have been compromised; the beam was then moved over to align with the piston rod, thus putting it out of alignment with the air pump resulting in the need to bend the air pump rod to a 3″ offset. The other end of the beam is out of alignment with the crankshaft and the sweep rod is therefore not vertical.

Restoration: The Engine into Steam Again

At the Council Meeting of the Trevithick Society in August 1984 it was proposed that the 50th anniversary celebrations of the Society be centred around the Levant engine with the object of opening the engine to the public. During a visit to the engine members were appalled by its condition. So, in the November Newsletter, having obtained the permission of the National Trust, the Hon. Secretary invited members to join a working

Top: some of the original Levant volunteers
Front, left-right: John Corin, Clive Carter, Mike Tarrant
Back, left-right: Ken Rosewall, Gerald Williams, Jonathan Rosewall, Dennis Jenkin

party on Saturday 1st December to begin cleaning and painting the engine. It soon became obvious that the task was greater man anticipated and that an opening date in 1985 was out of the question. Under the direction of Clive Carter, the old paint, a mixture of graphite and bitumen, was removed and by the spring of 1986 the engine was painted in a buff colour, like that used on the superstructure of naval auxiliary vessels (some wag suggested that the paint fell off the back of a minesweeper!).

In 1986 the National Trust began the restoration of the building, renewing the roof, re-pointing, providing handrails and a safer access path. By August 1987 the engine was painted in dark green with grey for the valve gear and the site opened to some 500 members of the public on six Sundays during August and September. Collecting boxes invited visitors to make donations, to be divided between the Society and the National Trust, this money covering much of the cost of the paint.

It was then suggested that the best means of preservation would be to put the engine to work. Discussions were held with the National Trust about steaming the engine. If it could be shown that the engine was capable of being moved then consideration would be given to raising sufficient funds to rebuild the boiler house and to provide a boiler. With Milton Thomas in charge of what had become known as the "Greasy Gang" — a term first coined by Giles Clotworthy, the National Trust's Public Relations Officer — the engine was refurbished, with advice from Consultant Engineers, the support of John Treloar, the engineer commissioned by the National Trust, and a great deal of hard work and ingenuity by the Greasy Gang. Help came from members and local firms, including Geevor Tin Mine who supplied equipment and parts, Cornwall Technical College which refurbished parts in the Engineering Department, English China Clays which donated a Cornish boiler, the Daniel brothers who transported the boiler behind their Burrell traction engine, and many others. The result of many months of work was that the engine moved on compressed air.

The Levant Engine Appeal Committee was formed in 1990, with Lord Falmouth as President, with members from the National Trust, the Trevithick Society and others supporting the project. Designs for a poster by Colin Fearon were approved (a poster which has been used every year since) together with the Appeal Letterhead. Peter Mansfield, Senior Land Agent for the National Trust (later Regional Director) confirmed that National Trust Headquarters had given approval for the project.

Sources of Grant Aid were discussed together with estimates of cost. The Fulton steam

The second greasy Greasy Gang (left-right): Courtney Rowe, Martin Beckett, Milton Thomas, Tom Barr, Michael Ladner, Eric King, Bill Miles, unknown; the shadow on the right may belong to Ken Stead.

The boiler being loaded onto a lorry for transport off the Trethowel site.

plant alone would cost some £14,000 plus a further £5,000 for installation. The target figure was agreed at £75,000 nett, £95,000 overall. The National Trust appointed John Kilroy as fund raiser, and John Dalton as Architect. The Appeal was formally launched in September 1990 in a marquee set up on ground above the engine house, with full coverage from local Press and TV. An application for a European Architecture Heritage Grant was made for submission to Brussels in 1991. The Appeals list was circulated to all National Trust members in Cornwall, to National Trust Associations in UK and overseas, to National Trust supporters, members of the Trevithick Society, and others, in all over 12,000. The National Trust as owners of the site made applications for a Rural Development Grant. But the National Trust could not place a contract for the boiler house until funds had been underwritten. It was suggested that when the Appeal reached three quarters of the target it might be possible to obtain a loan from Central funds, to be met by further responses to the Appeal. Donations totalled £10,000, plus £12,000 from the Rural Development Commission and £5,000 from the Manifold Trust.

By November 1991 when the total cost of the project was put at £128,000; £15,000 had been raised plus the RDC £12,000, the European Architectural Award of 22% of cost, *i.e.* £27,000, £20,000 from the Midland Bank Affinity Card Scheme and £5,000 from Penwith District Council, 80% of the cost was now available on deposit. There was now no doubt about the ability to go forward, but a determined effort was needed to assure £30 - 40,000 over the next five years. There would be proceeds from visitors to the site and this would depend on the Trevithick Society continuing to provide stewards on a voluntary basis. In November 1991 Peter Mansfield and Bill Newby travelled to Brussels to receive the European Architectural Award by which time building work on the restoration was nearing completion, ahead of schedule, with landscape work and access routes to be completed in the following months.

In August 1992 the Fulton boiler raised steam for the first time and adjustments were made. The engine steamed for the first time on 30th March 1993. That same month a totally unexpected but very welcome donation to the Appeal of £10,000 was made by the Mary Webb Trust. This brought the Appeal closer to its target. The balance, currently supported by an interest free loan arranged by the National Trust would be met from entrance fees and be paid off sooner than expected.

At noon on Monday, June 28th 1993 the National Trust organised a gathering of all those involved in the restoration. Lord Falmouth, President of the Appeal Committee, and the Trevithick Society, called the restored engine, "A fitting memorial to the men who worked so long ago at these mines". A plaque to commemorate the event and the efforts of the Greasy Gang was presented to Milton Thomas to be sited on the top floor of the engine house. Finally, in March 1994, Bruce Millan, European Commissioner for Regional Policy unveiled a plaque which acknowledged the work of the Society, the numerous gifts, and substantial grants. The Trevithick Society continues to provide stewards and guides at Levant, whilst the ever-changing Greasy Gang meets every Friday throughout the year with a rolling programme of maintenance and improvements. The National Trust with grant aid and receipts from visitors undertakes a programme of

Crowds at Levant to greet the arrival of the new boiler.

85

conservation and improvements to the site.

The National Trust owned only the Levant engine and house, but the rest of the site was owned by Geevor Mine. An offer was made in 1992 to buy the Carron Becander electric winder for its scrap value, but the scrap man had already decided to remove it through the roof of the house on the same day that the Trethowel boiler (which had been donated to the Trevithick Society by the then English China Clays Company) was craned onto its footings in the re-built boiler house. To facilitate removal the bed-plate of the winder was cut in half. The air compressor and air receiver were also removed and these were sold, but the winder remained at Geevor covered in plastic sheeting.

The original 110v electrical supply to the engine house was cut off when Geevor ceased mining operations. A small portable generator was supplied to enable the Greasy Gang to work with power tools but in 1992 a three-phase generator was put in the adjacent winder shed to power the new steam plant, oil and water pumps and lighting. This shed had been built to house a small electric winder brought from Malaya and wound from the original head frame. The generator was removed after mains electricity was available and the shed was used as a store and workshop. It is now the Video Room.

The custodian and volunteers knew that there was great potential to expand the Levant experience to visitors. The existence, but not the condition, of the man engine tunnel and shaft was known. Both the shaft and the spiral stairway leading from the miners' dry to

The newly-constructed boiler house; landscaping is still to be completed.

the tunnel were filled with rubbish and in the summer of 1996 this was partially cleared. During these diggings a number of iron double hooks were found. These must have been thrown in when the building was demolished and photographs of the dry shows these hooks positioned over the steam pipes above the miners' lockers. Limited access was gained into the tunnel but it was not possible to get right up the shaft because of more rubble, although the tunnel appeared to be in very good condition. The spiral stairway was re-filled to prevent unauthorised entry.

Various other excavations were carried out. Because Levant is on a metered water supply a leat was constructed, starting from a spring near to the old compressor house, and a series of closed pipes and open launders made to feed water to the cooling pond. This water keeps the engine condenser cool and helps maintain a vacuum in the engine for efficient and economical running. What appears to be an inspection pit for traction engines was also uncovered just to the east of the dry. Other excavations revealed a flywheel slot, a curious arched duct near the count house, and a large coil of decaying winding rope, consisting of wrought iron strands with a hemp core, showing that hemp has a longer life than iron under coastal conditions. A number of improvements and adjustments were carried out during the early years of putting the whim to work, amongst these was the addition of a compound gauge. This enables the driver and visitors to see either the steam pressure or the vacuum within the cylinder.

On the 12th January 1995 the National Trust held a flag raising ceremony at all their properties to celebrate Centenary of the Trust's foundation. At Levant the flag was raised by the Right Reverend Brian Coombes, Grand Bard of the Cornish Gorseth. The occasion was also used to commemorate those who lost their lives in the Man Engine disaster of October 1919. Major White's punch and saffron buns were served to the visitors. There was a further ceremony as a time capsule was buried beneath the slate covering the side flues of the boiler. The capsule contained copies of *The Cornishman*, *The Western Morning News*, the National Trust's *Cornish Engines* and Trevithick Society publications *Levant, a Champion Cornish Mine*, *Cornish Beam Engines and Rotative Winding Engines*, the four Levant postcards, the Guides to the Engine and the Walkabout, together with other leaflets and brochures. These events also marked thirty years of co operation between the Society and the Trust.

In 1996 the Trevithick Society was awarded a PRISM grant (fund for the Preservation of Industrial and Scientific Material) from the Science Museum for the purchase and restoration of the Levant head frame, and for the purchase of the electric winder plus the cost of crane hire and transport. The winder was in very poor condition due to having been left in the open during the previous four years. The bed-plate had to be welded together again and an intensive degree of de-rusting carried out. When the winder was craned out originally damage was caused by the slings used for hoisting.

It was the ambition of the volunteers to restore the winder and to operate it under its original controls. In order to do this the electrical circuit had to be redesigned because

Fred Dibnah and Dick Snell in the engine house in 2002.

aspects of the original equipment and circuitry were no longer to be used. Although there was three-phase power within the winder house, the power available was limited so it was not possible to use the original 35 horse-power induction motor. A smaller motor was fitted out of sight within the brake pit and an air compressor installed to operate the post brake. Some parts of the winder are still missing to this day, including the tacho-generator and the travelling-light telegraph. The tacho-generator was driven from the main gear box and this fed a voltage to a rope speed indicator and recorder. The telegraph informed the driver if the cage was not moving. This was a well-known phenomenon in the downward direction as the cage was notorious for jamming within the shaft and leaving a coil of slack cable above it! This was because Skip Shaft is crooked and at several points the men riding the cage were used to jumping up and down to free it from the runners as it ran around bends within the shaft. This was a potentially dangerous situation for the riders in the cage. The electric winder was installed by Geevor Mine with a cage that could carry four men and/or materials to the level connecting Levant to Geevor and the new incline shaft.

During 1996 lighting was installed in both Skip and Engine shafts and this always impressed visitors when they looked down. The old ladder-road consisting of 98 ladders in Skip Shaft can also be viewed, although only the top two stages are visible. During 2006 Robin and Charlie Daniel used Swedish pine to refurbish Skip Shaft and its sollars, so there is now safe access to adit level, though not for members of the public. The upcast fan in Engine Shaft, previously used by Geevor for ventilation and radon extraction, was freed up and a small electric motor fitted. It is now awaiting refurbishment and is no longer run for demonstration purposes.

October 20th 1999 was the 80th anniversary of the man-engine disaster. A memorial service was held by the Reverend Kathy Smith and was attended by the Cape Singers and many local people including Elaine George (the then Town Clerk of St Just) whose grandfather was killed in the accident. The event was recorded for broadcast on local television.

Since the beginning of the Levant restoration great interest has been generated by National Trust publications and coverage by the Press and television. Fred Dibnah came to Levant on three occasions, the first on 23rd June 1998. There is nothing new about Levant Mine appearing in films or television, no doubt helped by its spectacular setting at the top of the cliffs. "Love Story" starring Stewart Granger and Margaret Lockwood was partly filmed at Levant in 1944, and the BBC Series "Poldark" starring Robin Ellis and Angharad Rees used Levant in one of its scenes in 1974. The front and end of the electric winder house were covered in hardboard on a flimsy timber framework and painted to resemble a count house. Parts of Series 3 of Poldark were also filmed onsite in 2014.

In 1999 there were problems with the whim. The cylinder had begun to lean, which caused the piston to run out of alignment. Packing was put under the cylinder but the problem soon re-occurred. It was also discovered that the foundations of the granite bedstone under the cylinder were unstable.

The condenser and air pump are located in a timber cistern in a pit ten feet deep immediately in front of the iron cylinder. The timber cistern containing the condenser was leaking badly and an examination of the underside revealed the supporting timbers had almost rotted away. Cast concrete pillars and timber supports were put in place to support the cistern for the following year whilst plans were made to replace the cistern at the end of 1999. During the original restoration the cistern had been sealed internally with concrete to overcome the leaks. Another problem that had been apparent for some time was the continual movement of the main cylinder.

The National Trust employed two specialist builders, Colin Rashleigh and Owen Pascoe, to carefully remove the cistern and dig out the concrete surrounding the condenser, whilst John Treloar and Norman Lackford did the mechanical work.

After removing the cistern, by taking the weight of the condenser on a series of chain blocks, it was possible to look into the void under the main cylinder. It was then that Milton Thomas's famous words "Nothing is easy at Levant" were remembered. The cylinder was found to be resting on a bedstone over a granite infill supported by a series of granite lintels through which the cylinder hold down bolts pass. All the granite lintels were cracked and starting to collapse,

Norman Lackford working during the 2000 rebuild of the hotwell and condenser.

89

John Treloar and Dick Snell servicing the reduction valve.

the cylinder retaining bolts were badly rusted and this was the cause of the cylinder movement. As this could affect the structural integrity of the engine house, the National Trust sought advice from a structural engineer who recommended casting a new base for the cylinder, keyed into the engine house walls together with installation of a series of steel girders to support the front of the pit that contained the condenser and air pump.

The stairs and all guards and other obstructions were removed for access and so it began.... The first task was to remove the condenser and air pump assembly. This sounds simple enough but with the sides of the cistern removed it was noticed that the front wall of the pit was hanging and unstable and had to be propped. The rust joint between the condenser and outlet valve chest manifold took three days to break! The work started by drilling and ended by hand chiselling. The joint was found to be a mixture of modern Belzona, used during restoration, covering an original rust joint supported by lead fillets. Having eventually removed the joint, the condenser and air pump were lowered enough to separate from the manifold then be swung aside and lifted to floor level to be parked alongside the flywheel.

The main cylinder complete with valves and manifold had to be raised by about two feet to give access to its mounting base. The lift was carried out with a series of chain blocks suspended from the beam. The beam had to be supported at intervals along its entire length to ensure no damage occurred. The bob loft floor, in turn had to be supported from below by props to spread the load (estimated to be about 5 tonnes) as evenly as possible whilst this delicate operation took place. By lifting with a series of chain blocks the cylinder assembly could be lifted and steered horizontally and vertically to manoeuvre it away from the unstable pit wall. It was then raised two feet above the bedstone. It is a sad reflection on British industry that the chain blocks, strops and shackles were all made in China. How far have we come since 1840?

With the engine out of the way the real work started. The first job was to remove the bedstone prior to building a new base under the cylinder. With the precarious pit wall shored up, no further lifting capacity within the building and no firm floor or access for a crane, the bedstone had to be broken up in place by drilling prior to its removal. This was very controversial at the time and produced letters to local newspapers but with the lifting and access limitations there was no other option. The broken bedstone can now be seen outside the boiler house.

After removal of the bedstone a wooden mould was constructed to cast a concrete re-placement cylinder mounting. This mounting was keyed into the engine house walls, is two feet deep and the complex matrix of reinforcing rods is a work of art, or as known in Cornwall "a proper job". The new cylinder hold-down bolts protrude through this base from the underside. Of course whilst all this took place the cylinder was suspended only two feet above the new base leaving very little space for Colin Rashleigh and Owen Pascoe to perform their concrete magic. With the base complete the front wall of the pit was supported by girders bolted to stainless steel rods passing through the base to the outside wall of the engine house.

The pit was excavated by a further two or three feet but only silt was found and so two concrete lintels were again cast from wall to wall across the pit to support the new timber cistern. The cistern, made of pine, was prefabricated and pre-drilled in sections, then brought to the engine house as a series of planks to be reassembled in the pit. It copies the original method of construction and dimensions as far as possible but using stainless steel truss rods and galvanised bolts. The stainless nuts had to be specially made, as the original nuts were square. The cistern had to be assembled and bolted together in one day as each joint was sealed with mastic and the complete assembly bolted up before it set. Finally it was coated with several layers of a bitumen compound.

The concrete took 28 days to cure before any load could be placed upon it and during this time the condenser and air pump assembly was de-rusted, cleaned and painted. The original casting was very poor and many holes had been plugged with lead during its construction. The base is a separate casting and both the air pump and the condenser are joined to the base by rust joints.

Once the concrete had cured the air pump/condenser was lowered down into the cistern, and we attempted to align it. We found that it was not possible to align the air pump centrally once the condenser was inserted into the valve chest manifold without the manifold fouling the side of the air pump. This is the reason why the air pump rod had always been offset by a 3″ bend immediately under the

The new cylinder bedstone, built in 2000.

91

beam. This had always been a problem causing considerable vibration when the engine is in operation. However during this initial attempt at reassembly it was found that the condenser which had, by now, been dry for nearly 6 months, was showing signs of a crack in the rust joint between the condenser and the base. Further examination showed fracture of the original rust joint and so the condenser was separated from its base and pulled back up.

The hot well and condenser back in the cistern.

A close examination of the rust joint showed that it appeared to have remained active and had eroded much of the parent metal. The wall thickness of the condenser vessel was less than 1/8″ thick in some parts. In view of the poor quality cast iron it was not possible to weld the condenser back to its base so a sleeve was made to bolt them together. The sleeve was machined from a solid steel billet that was so heavy that John Treloar, the National Trust engineer, had to lift it into his lathe with chain blocks. This took a week to turn and bore. The machining of the condenser and its mating face took three days and produced much thick black dust.

As the sleeve had to be turned from solid it was decided to make it eccentric to cure the alignment problem by offsetting the condenser on its base. By reassembling in place in the cistern, all that was needed was to align the air pump and rotate the eccentric sleeve for correct condenser alignment. This has enabled the correct alignment of the air pump and condenser separately before joining and in consequence it was possible to replace the old bent and cracked pump rod with a new straight rod, removing a lot of the vibration that had plagued the engine for many years. Once the sleeve was fitted the joints were completed with a modern epoxy based compound to replicate the original rust joints. The base of the condenser and air pump was bolted through the cistern to a steel channel on the underside with much difficulty (only Colin Rashleigh was slim enough to get under the cistern and turn the bolts). John Treloar made up the clamping ring to bolt around the base of the air pump to enable it to be bolted down in the cistern at low level for increased stability. The underside of the air pump and condenser assembly was sealed to the cistern with an epoxy sealer to prevent any leaks from its fragile cast iron base.

The cylinder and valve chest assembly was finally lowered into place and after the rust joint between the condenser and manifold was completed we were able to reconstruct the floor timbers and remount the valve actuating gear and brake operating arms in their correct positions. The engine finally went back into steam for the first time on a Saturday afternoon in an empty engine house, but all the workers were pleased and very relieved when it ran from the very first pull of the steam valve, with no major problems. All that was left to do was to adjust the valve lift and clearances and cure a small leak on the dump valve that was causing excessive water admission to the condenser.

Finally, after the mess was cleared out and the guards were put back, the engine was run by setting the steam valve on

Above: the damaged drum removed.

Below: the axle being very carefully skimmed.

the peg and leaving it to run by itself. It ran for a full hour on the peg without any adjustment to the steam valve. It finally reopened to the public on 10th September and the engine successfully steamed for the whole of 2001. The only major problem left was the main axle or beam pivot that was suspected to be bent and this was be done during the winter of 2001.

John Treloar also had to fabricate new mounting brackets for the brake, dump valve and floor mountings, all of which took time and careful measurement. Much of the work

The new depth indicator, now in the engine house.

was in the condenser pit or under the suspended cylinder assembly with very little access. It took three days crouching in the timber cistern to grind the old rust joints away and three weeks to get clean after. The cast iron dust penetrates overalls, clothes and skin, and leaves a tidemark on the bath that has to be removed with abrasive compound. Quite what the old men who built these engines endured, working with candles, oil lamps and hand tools is beyond belief.

Since 2005 the landward-side winding drum had been loose on its shaft and this was causing noise when the engine was running. After several unsuccessful attempts, work was carried out during the winter of 2006/7 to replace all the rusted bolts with new galvanised ones in preparation for the removal of the drum should this be found necessary. Copper packing was inserted to enable the drum to be re-tightened onto the shaft, but further works were needed to secure the drum. A working replica of the level indicator has now been constructed and can be seen above the bottom of the stairs in the engine house.

The year 2009 turned out to be a very busy one, particularly regarding work on the whim. For several years the Greasy Gang had tried different methods of securing the landward side winding drum to the shaft. It frequently moved towards the engine house wall which if it touched, could have done tremendous damage or even wrecked the engine. Various shims and packing pieces were tried but because of heavy corrosion on the shaft, nothing lasted very long. It was therefore decided to remove both of the drums by crane and refurbish them both and skim the shaft down to bare metal. Metal Surgery of Penryn carried out the removal, in conjunction with South West Cranes and the project was recorded with photographs and video shot by Ron Flaxman and John Potter. After removal it was discovered that only one section of the four halves (two halves per drum) was undamaged. Two flanges had major fractures within them and two halves had cracks running for about ninety degrees around their circumference; this was only obvious once the drums had been shot-blasted. Steel has been inserted internally and metal stitching carried out to all of the cracks and the shaft was refaced. New split 'top-hat' bushes were manufactured to fit between the drums and the shaft. The final cost of the project was on the order of £30,000.

June 7th 2009 was the 25th anniversary of the start of the restoration of the winding engine by the 'Greasy Gang'. The engine was in steam and free admission and guided tours were granted to all. Attractions on site included a coast guard display, local radio, steam traction engine, classic cars and Cornish crafts. Although the weather was damp and windy we had about 500 through the doors that day, with many offering donations and buying raffle tickets.

Finally, on October 20th the 90th Anniversary of the Man-engine disaster was held. The sun shone for the day with about 200 people attending, including Levant employees and volunteers and Pendeen School children, some wearing the costumes of miners and bal-maidens. The local minister Reverend Roger Greene read the names of the 31 miners who died that day and as each name was read, a child came forward and placed a white rose at the top of the spiral staircase leading to the man-engine tunnel and shaft. The Cape Singers were also in attendance and they began the proceedings with Cousin Jack and concluded with Working Man. The Reverend Colin Short (a Levant guide and Trevithick Society member) read the Lord's Prayer, and the site was open free of charge with the engine in steam.

Some of the Levant volunteers and members of staff in 2014. *Photo by Lisetta Laird.*

Back, left-right: Jan Beare, Terry Nankervis, Stuart Abell, Anita Pryor, Caroline Schofield, Jenny Pirrin, John Cass, John Machray, Stephen Tucker, Stuart Keast, Adrian Felix, Len Phillips, Chris Quick, George Blenkhorne.

Front, left-right: Pete Joseph, Ryan Thomas, Hylda Harker, Ted Mole, Anthony Power, Ron Flaxman, Pete Badger.

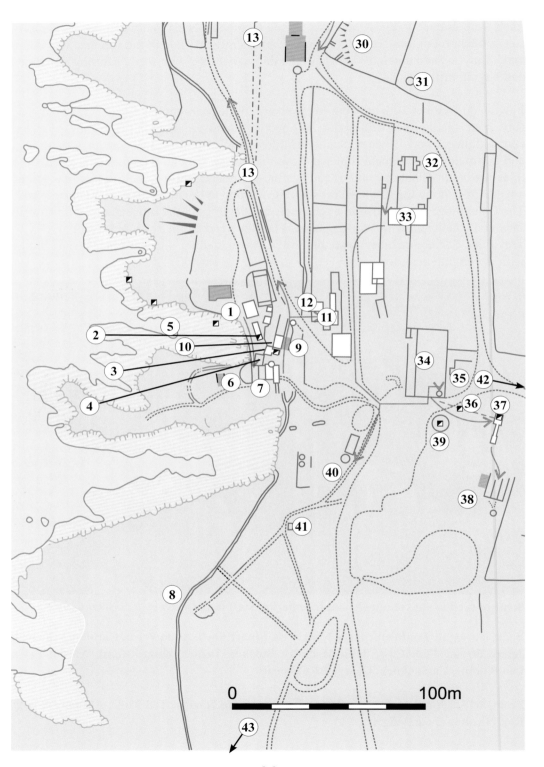

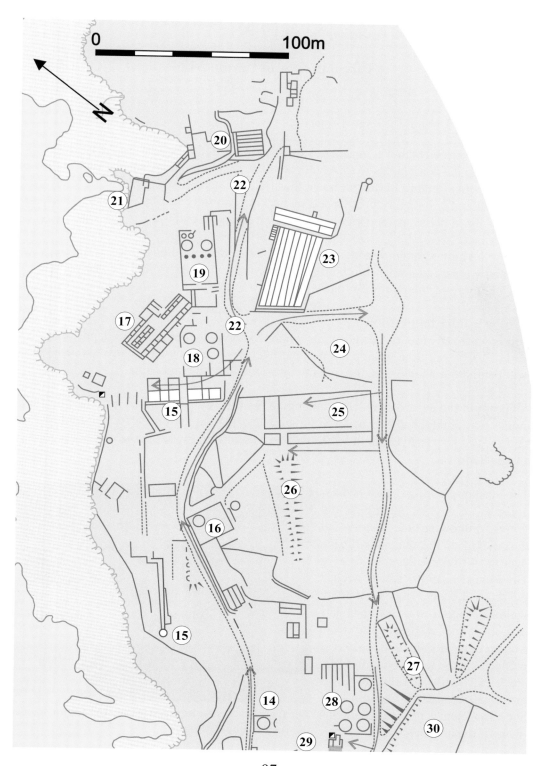

Chapter 11

A Circular Tour of Levant Mine

The tour described below begins at Levant's reception and follows a clockwise direction, firstly along the coast path and then along another path through the site to finish at the car park. The final feature in the guide, Higher Bal, lies nearly half a kilometre south west of Levant and is probably best visited by parking carefully nearby in Levant Road. All features listed below are shown on the maps on pages 96 and 97.

Levant is a ruined mine; it comprises partly dismantled buildings, piles of rubble often hidden by grass, and other rough ground. Except for the area around the engine houses, sensible footwear may prevent injury.

1. New winder house/shop

This is where any tour of Levant starts, where you bought your tickets and, probably, this book. Please take time to look around; there are books to buy and things to see. On the wall behind the winding engine is some information on Levant Mine.

Adjacent to the exit is a model beam engine, worked by compressed air. The part-built model was completed by Levant volunteers and the engine house scratch-built to the same scale. This is an example of the engine which formerly sat in the derelict pumping engine house.

The centre-piece of the winder house is, of course, the engine and drums. Following the success of the sealing of the undersea breach over the 40-fathom level by Geevor Tin Mines in 1966, it was needed to drain Levant, and a modern winding engine was erected. The new machine was acquired from Carron Becander in 1970; unlike its predecessors, the new engine was electrically driven. Skip Shaft was refurbished to the 190 fathom level and a four-man cage was installed in place of the original two ore skips.

The Carron - Becander electric hoisting engine inside the winder house/shop.

Adit level

50

100

150

200

250

278
290

50 fathoms

2. Skip Shaft

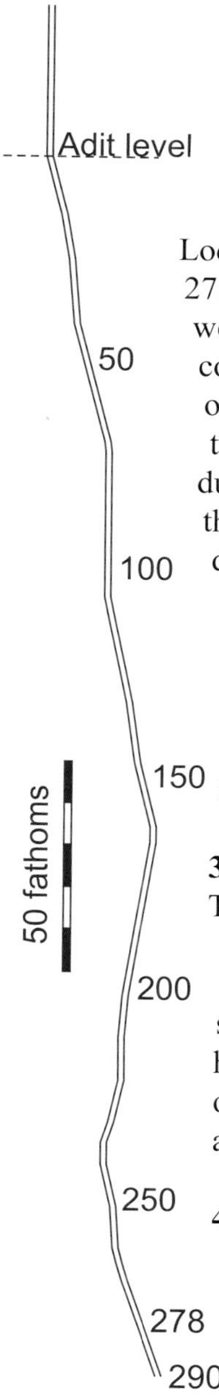

Following the footpath left out of the winder house, Skip Shaft and its headframe are on the left. Go into the building and look down the shaft. Some information on the shaft, including a diagram showing the various bends, can be seen on the wall. The 10′ by 4½′ shaft was sunk on Old Bal Lode and is thought to be 290 fathoms deep below adit. The bottom level is the 278, the main tramming level, also known as the Pony level as these beasts were used to haul wagons there. The adit is at 35 fathoms depth below the shaft collar. Skip Shaft, like many other Cornish shafts, was sunk on the underlie of Old Bal Lode; this means that it followed the dip of the lode. Not only was the ground here usually softer than the other country rock, but the ore found during the sinking probably paid for the sinking. Unfortunately this also meant that the angle of the shaft changed in amount and direction, as shown in the diagram on the left.

Above the shaft is the rather peculiar timber covered head frame. Usually head frames are actual frames but this has a plywood covering, the result of the shaft being utilised in later years as part of the Geevor underground ventilation control system. The headframe was built by Geevor Tin Mines in 1966; it is a Grade II Listed Building.

3. Engine Shaft

This shaft was also sunk on Old Bal Lode and is also thought to be 290 fathoms deep below adit; it also measures 10′ by 4½′. The shaft is hidden inside a building which extends from the front of the engine house to the seaward side. This building also houses the now disused updraught fan which helped ventilate the mine. The shaft itself can be seen behind a grille, lit for observation. At surface the shaft was equipped with a headframe, also known as a shears, sadly no longer present.

4. The film room

Take some time to stop here and watch a film on the history of Levant Mine.

5. Levant Zawn

After coming out of the Skip Shaft building, take a look over the railings at Levant Zawn. The mine's principal adit is here, reached by a tortuous path down the cliff. Batten's Shaft is low down on the cliff, just outside the adit. The mine's first pumping engine was installed on the slope above Batten's Shaft (below the reservoir), from which it pumped, probably hoisting water in kibbles. Phillips Shaft is also near the base of the cliff, about 60m further north.

The deep cleft to the south is Boscregan Zawn, where Boscregan Lode outcrops. The word zawn is a local term, most usually applied to a narrow inlet formed by erosion along a line of weakness, such as a lode or fault. The exception to this is Wheal Edward Zawn at Botallack, which is very wide and shallow, almost the opposite of all the others.

6. Reservoir

This reservoir provided water for the engine's condenser. In Newcomen's original steam engine design, pressure of the atmosphere was used to work an engine. A piston with a connecting rod moved inside a cylinder. Steam was then passed into the cylinder under the piston; the cylinder was then cooled and the steam inside was condensed to water. A partial vacuum is created under the cylinder and the pressure of the air pushes the piston down powerfully. Unfortunately this method of condensing meant that the cylinder was alternately heated and cooled at each stroke, meaning that part of the steam's potential was lost at each stroke.

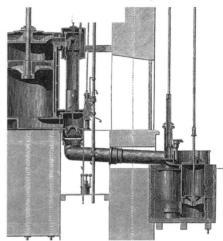

The condenser, attached to the cylinder (left), leading to the hotwell, outside the engine house (right).

James Watt introduced the separate condenser. The atmospheric engine was very inefficient and used a lot of fuel. The cylinder was heated up by the steam and then cooled each time the piston moved. Watt improved the engine by taking the used steam into a condenser outside the cylinder. The steam cooled, condensed, and the cylinder did not have to be reheated. Later, Watt found that he could use steam below the piston and vacuum above to pull the piston up and then steam above and vacuum below to push the piston down. This is called a double acting engine. This type of engine was used to turn winding drums and operate stamps; these are known as rotative engines.

7. The Levant Whim

The Levant 24-inch all-indoor double-acting beam winding engine was acquired in

1840 and probably replaced a 20-inch engine which hoisted from Batten's Shaft, lower down the cliff. It was designed by Francis Michell of Redruth and built by Harvey & Co. of Hayle. The new engine hoisted from Skip Shaft, to the rear of the engine house and just a few metres away **The exterior of the whim engine house showing the two drums pointing towards the Skip Shaft headframe in the background.**

The whim engine. At the far end is the top of the engine cylinder and the valve gear. The piston rod from the top of the engine connects with the beam in the top chamber. In the foreground the cast-iron rod connects the end of the beam to the crank, which turns the winding drums outside the engine house via the flywheel on the left.

from the pumping engine shaft; at some, currently unknown point in its life it was recylindered to 27-inches. This is the only Cornish beam winding engine in the world which is in steam in its original engine house.

The shaft is 290 fathoms deep below the adit. This engine was saved from being scrapped in 1935, the house being one of the only two to survive the mine's closure. This type of engine house is comparatively unusual: all of the engine, including its beam was inside, and it is one of only two remaining in Cornwall complete with walls.

Inside the rebuilt boiler house (the original house was demolished) is a Holman Brothers Cornish boiler built in 1900. The boiler was generously donated by ECC Quarries Ltd. and was removed and transported from Trethowel Wood, St. Austell, in the summer of 1990. This boiler is similar to the type as used by the mine in its working days; it is for display purposes only, the steam being generated by a modern plant behind the scenes.

The reciprocating engine was attached to a flywheel which in turn was connected, through one of the walls, to a pair of drums. Originally these would have had cast-iron chains wound around them, but the chains were replaced by flat hempen rope after an unsuccessful trial of wire rope in about 1860. Following the accident at Botallack Mine in 1865, where the chain used for hoisting men through the Boscawen Diagonal Shaft broke, killing eight men and a boy, wire rope was used throughout

The beam in the upper chamber. The engine cylinder is beneath the nearer end. Note that the beam was cast in two halves.

Cornwall. From the winding drums (often called 'cages' on Cornish mines) the chain or rope went to the top of the headframe and round a sheave wheel, then down the shaft. Ore from the mine was brought up in cast iron buckets known as kibbles. Being of a comparatively soft material they were prone to wearing out by scraping along the sides of the shafts.

Come out of the boiler house and take some time to admire Boscregan Zawn.

8. Levant leat

Water was an important commodity on Cornish mines, being required for the dressing of ores. Sometimes water was pumped to surface for use on mines, which took place at Levant, however it was also distributed by means of leats. Water for Levant came from Spearne Moor Mine about half a kilometre to the south-west. Possibly it was collected from the small stream here but it may also have come from one of the mine's adits.

The leat extends around the coast, in places the route was blasted through rock while in other places a timber launder was suspended from the rocks on chains. In some places the leat has been lost through erosion but much remains. The main destination of this leat was the reservoir for the winding and pumping engines however the leat can be traced further north where it supplied either dressing floors or a waterwheel or, possibly, both.

The Levant leat, close to its source; the rock has been cut to allow passage round the cliffs.

After looking at the leat, turn left around the side of the boiler house. On the left is a square piece of granite with four bolts, one near each corner. This is the original bedstone for the cylinder of the whim engine.

9. Pumping engine boiler house

On leaving the whim engine house or boiler house, turn left; the path goes through the site of the pumping engine's boiler house. This building formerly housed a single Cornish boiler, of the type developed by Richard Trevithick in 1812. The earlier "wagon" or "haystack" boilers were heated from beneath, just like kettles, and any scale or impurities that formed a sediment settled upon this plate, insulating it from the water. This reduced heating efficiency and could lead to local overheating and failure of the boiler plates. In addition, these boilers only produced steam at a pressure of a few pounds per square inch.

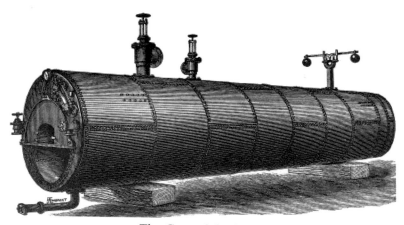

The Cornish boiler is a long horizontal cylinder with a single large flue containing the fire. As the furnace relied on natural draught, a tall chimney was required at the far end of the flue to encourage a good supply of air

The Cornish boiler.

(oxygen) to the fire. For efficiency, Trevithick's innovation was to encase beneath the boiler with a brick-built chamber. Exhaust gases passed through the central flue and then routed outside and around the iron boiler shell. To keep the chimney clear of the firing space, the brick flue passed first underneath the centre of the boiler to the front face, then back again along the sides and to the chimney.

Coal for the boiler was delivered via a chute in the wall from the track above.

To the right of the Engine Shaft is the site of a shaft capstan. This was used to manually raise and lower equipment up and down the shaft for maintenance. The capstan had a vertical axle, around which was a long length of rope which ran along the ground in a channel and then upwards to the small head frame, known as a shears, over a pulley wheel and down the shaft. A number of arms, though usually not more than six, were fixed to the top of the axle to enable men

Image of boiler house site showing balance bob pit and coal chute.

to turn the capstan. Shaft capstans could be dangerous when the rope was overloaded; in the case when the load ran away men could be thrown great distances and badly injured; in a number of cases there were fatalities. In addition, the site of the balance bob for the pitwork in the Engine Shaft can be seen.

10. Pumping engine house

By 1835 Levant Mine had acquired a 40-inch pumping engine; the foundry is unknown

Engraving of a pumping engine from the Harvey & Co. catalogue of 1884.

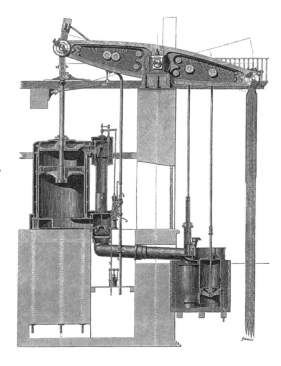

but it seems likely to have been built by Harvey & Co. in Hayle. It was certainly Harvey & Co. which supplied the 45-inch engine which replaced the 40-inch engine in 1872 (there is also a possibility that the old engine was recylindered); it was installed by Messrs. Eustice & Son, the mine's engineer. The house is one of the oldest surviving in the St Just district and is Listed Grade II*.

The engine house, although modified and now missing its boiler house, is still nearly complete, the floor showing that it was originally tiled. When the beam was being removed from the house in about 1935 it jammed, and had to be dynamited to free it. Such treatment was common when an engine was to be scrapped. When an engine was to be moved to another mine or engine house, the large granite stones used for the cylinder loadings were also removed; if not, the bolts were cut to free the cylinder. By this means it is possible to tell the ultimate fate of a mine's engine. The stack is truncated, having been cut down in the 1960s during the breach sealing operations; possibly it was in the way.

At the front of the interior of the house is the cataract pit, or cockpit. Usually this would have contained a floor intermediate between the bottom of the pit and the floor of the engine house

The pumping engine house. In the centre of the wall is the door from the boiler house. The long bar hanging from the left-hand side of the wall would have been attached to the now-missing shears to help stabilise it. The thick wall nearest the shaft is the bob wall while the two side walls are called wing walls. At the rear of the house is an arched opening called the cylinder door, which is the opening through which the engine cylinder was brought into the house.

(the cylinder plat). The cataract pit contained the apparatus for regulating the engine and also gave access to the hold-down bolts which held the engine cylinder down onto its loadings and granite bedstones.

Because of the crookedness of the Engine Shaft, it required five angle bobs to alter the angle of the timber beam in the shaft. These were at surface (which was actually a balance bob), 54, 78, 110 and 130 fathoms; catch-wings, similar to those fitted to the man-engine, were fitted to the pit work to stop it falling into the shaft in case the beam or pitwork broke.

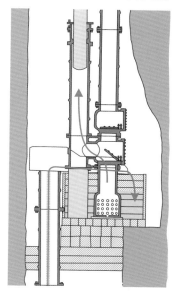

Removing water from the mine was obviously very important, so how did the beam engine do the work? The coastal mines of the St Just district were lucky in that the volcanic rocks (greenstones) on the coast are very dense and impervious to water. However, most of Levant Mine was not in this rock but water percolated through the granite and killas, particularly along the lodes, where the rock was fractured, and this collected in the mine. Water was channelled along the levels in a series of leats and launders to the shaft and allowed to flow to the bottom to the sump.

It is a common misconception that the beam engine was the actual pump; this is incorrect, it was the engine which operated the pumping equipment in the shaft. Water from the sump was pumped up a rising main in the shaft by pumps operated by the pump rods

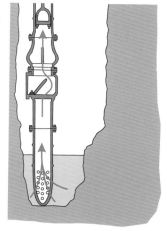

In the drawings here the pump rod is moving upwards. Water is drawn through a cast-iron egg-ended windbore which is perforated to allow water in but not stones. The valve at the bottom opens to allow water to pass and closes on the down stroke to stop water leaking back. Higher up the shaft (20 to 30 feet) the water is drawn into the displacement pump past the lower of two valves.

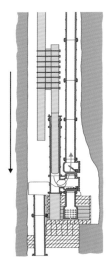

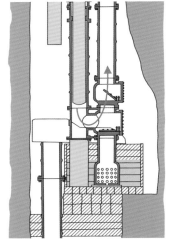

On the downstroke the water is pushed down the pump and upwards into the rising main to the next lift of pumps. The windbore is flat-bottomed but does the same job as the other one. The valves are known as 'clacks' because of the noise they made. The piece comprising the pump, windbore and rising main was known as an H-piece because of its shape,

(also known as 'pitwork') in the shaft, operated by the beam engine at surface. The beam engine itself was not the pump but merely the object that provided the motive power. Water was pumped from one pump to another, usually a distance of 20-30 fathoms. At the new pump it poured into a cistern and the process began again. Water was usually discharged into the adit but in some places, like Levant, water was also pumped to the surface for use on the dressing floors. The bottom lift of pumps was known as a 'bucket lift' as the water was physically raised by the upward stroke of the engine raising the pump which was directly worked by the pump rod; after reaching the lowest cistern the upward stroke sucked water from the

cistern into a displacement pump. The downward stroke of the engine pushed offset pieces of the pump rod into the displacement pump; this closed the lower valve and allowed water to be pumped up the rising main to the next lift.

One of the balance boxes in the Engine Shaft; this one is at adit level, with a Geevor miner for scale. Photograph taken in 1973 by Bryan Earl.

In about 1878 Levant acquired a steam pump from East Pool Mine for use in the sump in the submarine section. This pump was different from the beam engine in that it directly pumped the water instead of remotely working the pumps; it would have looked similar to the Evans pump in the shop/winder house. While these pumps are described as steam operated, many were actually worked by compressed air, which may have been the case here

11. Count House and Smithy

The count house formerly stood opposite the pumping engine house; this was the mine's office, where the purser and captains had their offices and was also where the adventurers held their meetings, heard the agents' reports and ate their sumptuous

Examples of tiles in the count house.

dinners. The present remains are in no way indicative of the former size and condition of the buildings, particularly the smithy, of which almost nothing remains. It is possible that other buildings exist here.

Investigation of the count house shows that it has been added to and modified a number of times. This is not unreasonable, and the bigger and more important the mine became, the bigger and more important became the count house. Some decorative floor tiles can be seen inside the remains of the building; areas of tiling are suggestive of a bathroom and toilets. As can be seen in various archive photos, the building was of two stories, comprising two conjoined double-fronted buildings and a single-storey building at right-angles to this. Three sets of bay windows can be seen in the photograph on page 33.

12. 1960s features
The breach sealing operations of the 1960s required various facilities to be constructed at Levant. Unfortunately, for Levant, the area chosen was one of the old copper dressing floors, which was completely destroyed. Several portakabins were constructed for offices and sheds for storage; just downslope of the count house is the site of the grout mixing plant. These buildings were removed once the breach was sealed and some permanent buildings constructed from concrete were put up to house the transformers and other facilities associated with the use of Skip Shaft as part of Geevor Tin Mines. Nothing now remains of these features except for a cement plinth and concrete wall just south of the count house; these are the only obvious evidence of an important phase in the recent history of Levant Mine.

13. Incline tramway to stamps
Copper ore from underground came up Skip Shaft and was delivered to the crusher and ore picking area, on the cliff side opposite the shop. Tin ore was trammed straight to the stamps, however as it had to go under the track it had to go through a short tunnel before going up the inclined tramway.

Incline tunnel in the foreground, passing under the photographer; the incline ascends uphill in the background.

The continuation of the tramway through the tunnel leads uphill to the Cornish stamps battery. Now it is one of the many footpaths across the site. Trams were hauled up the incline by a drive which was taken off the stamps axle.

14. Buddle: part of dressing floors

This single buddle is part of the main 19th century dressing floor (see 25, below). It is likely that other buddles were here and that some fragments of them remain to be found. It seems likely that the construction of the tramway has buried many features here.

15. Calciner stack, flues, chambers and Brunton Calciners

The calciner stack is the first part of the arsenic works to be reached, although it was last in the process.

The Levant labyrinth was almost completely destroyed and covered over in 1995 by what was then Cornwall County Council as it was considered a danger to the public. Unfortunately this decision had unforeseen circumstances. The material used came from a development at St Erth; unfortunately it was a slate-grey colour and the resultant dumped material became known as Pendeen airport, as it looked very much like a short runway. The material was then found to contain numerous detonators, some unused, and fragments of blasting cartridges. Many of these were removed and sent away for destruction and then the whole of the alien rock was taken away and local stone used.

The four Brunton calciners.

A fine, partly restored, and unusual labyrinth can be seen at Botallack, about a mile to the south. Unlike Levant, this labyrinth is a U-shape because of space constraints owing to the fact that it had to fit pre-existing structures.

To the north of the site lie the remains of the four Brunton calciners which roasted the ore

108

to remove its contaminating arsenic and sulphur. All of the calciners have a wide, arched, opening on one side known as the drive tunnel; line shafting passed through here to rotate the plate in the hearth. Narrow openings in the north side of each calciner was where the calcined ore, known as 'whits;, was discharged onto the 'hot floor' until it had cooled enough to continue processing the material.

These were damaged during and after the removal of their machinery while of the labyrinth and flues, which lie between the calciners and stack, almost nothing can be seen. The calciner stack is in good condition although a little shorter than when it was built. The calciners were originally powered by 24-foot diameter waterwheels, these being replaced by a 6hp Hornsby oil engine which was then replaced by a small horizontal engine. A length of flue can still be seen joining the stack.

16. Small building
This small building contained a single buddle inside a roughly square structure; possibly other features remain to be discovered. The building maybe associated with some settling strips to the south, nearly opposite the calciner stack.

17. Copper Precipitation Area
Just north of the calciners is the area where copper recovery took place. Copper oxide was treated with sulphuric acid to produce copper sulphate, with copper being precipitated out of the solution by scrap iron. This took place in some concrete-lined tanks set in a small yard.

The copper oxide was obtained by calcining what was termed 'foul ore', cassiterite (tin oxide) which was intimately mixed with copper sulphides. The copper produced was approximately in the ratio of 1:1.8 to the weight of iron lost during the copper precipitation. The sulphuric acid was apparently made on site, from the washing of the fumes from the calciners. One problem with this however is that there is no evidence for a

The copper precipitation area, just north of the calciners.

"scrubber" adjacent to the stack. Inside the scrubber a stream of water dissolved the sulphur dioxide from the calciner to form sulphuric acid.

Unfortunately most of the structures here are in a very poor condition. Copper precipitation was carried out at Levant and Botallack from the early 19th century and at Levant from the turn of the 20th century until its closure.

18. Dressing floor
This end of the site is where the final tin concentrate was produced up to the early 20th century. This small dressing floor, a few metres from the calciners, includes three buddles; it processed the material from the calciners.

19. 1922 dressing floor
The small dressing floor contains the massive loadings for an electro-magnetic separator, which was used to remove iron and manganese from the tin ore; two buddles lie just down hill. This mill probably dealt with the product of the larger 1922 mill, feature 22.

20. Settling/thickening strips
The very north part of the Levant site dealt with slimes. Formerly the site contained a number of round frames but these were replaced by more modern equipment, Mozley frames and Bartles' concentrators. Although this part of the site worked until the 1960s little now remains but for some slimes tanks on the west side of the footpath.

The water stamps. Tin ore was dropped down the slope on the right to run under the stamps; these were supported by the timber frame. The stamps were operated by a waterwheel behind the gabled wall. The stamped tin went to a catch-pit, where it was collected, possibly for further processing, however this would depend on the tenor of the ore.

21. Site of water stamps
Archive photographs show a set of Cornish stamps here in different stages of completion. These stamps crushed tin ore and were probably one of the earliest stamps on the mine. In latter years they were used to crush ore which had a high iron content and could not be processed with the normal run-of-mine ore. All that remains of the stamps today is the timber frame which helped keep the stamps upright. These stamps may have been used to crush ore from North Levant and Geevor, as Geevor was then called. The stamps were recorded by the photographer Geoffrey Ordish.

From here, return upslope past feature 19 and turn right. Continue uphill, past feature 18 (now on the right) and feature 19 (on the left). At the end of feature 19 turn left, then follow the footpath to the right, uphill, to see features 23 and onwards.

22. Tramway

In the late 19th-early 20th century a tramway was built at the north end of the site. This commenced at a point inland of the copper precipitation area and passed features 16 and 17. Just south of feature 17 the tramway disappeared, probably going through a cutting. The tramway reappeared north of feature 17 and ran a few metres further north. A branch of the tramway led west to a point near the water stamps. Most of the tramway seems to have been destroyed during the construction of the track, however part of the branch towards the water stamps can still be made out.

23. Settling/thickening strips

These cement-lined structures cover an area of approximately 53m by 27m. The walls between the strips widen towards the north, where the water was drained off into a set of smaller strips at a right-angle. These features have been cleared out and are in a very good condition. Geevor tailings were fed into these tanks, where they were de-watered. Water was then fed in along a flume over each tank, and mixed with the thickened slimes beneath to achieve the correct consistency. The mixture was then drained off and sent to the yard below, sent to tin frames then re-thickened and re-framed.

24. Heather field

This feature is probably unique to Levant Mine, although other mines may also have had them. The brushes of the buddles and round frames were edged with heather, and this field provided a local source.

25. 1922 mill

This building, with its many tall pillars, almost has the air of an Aztec temple. The pillars formerly supported the timber roof trusses of the building, while on the south side are the loadings for stamps. A mixture of different types were used here and when the mine closed it held 5 heads of Californian, six heads of Nissen and eight heads of Fraser & Chalmers stamps. Two heads of Holman pneumatic stamps had previously been installed; these were operated by compressed air and were much more efficient than either the Cornish or Californian types. A model of these stamps can be seen in the Geevor Museum. The mill would also have contained shaking tables and, probably, vanners. The loadings for the former can be seen in front of the

Part of the early 20th century mill showing the roof supports and loadings for Californian stamps. Geevor Mine is in the background.

stamps loadings, as well as several gutters. The mill also contained a number of vanning tables, of which only small marks can be seen to indicate their locations.

The mill has previously and erroneously been described as a wolfram (tungsten) mill, however wolframite, the common ore of tungsten, does not occur at either Levant or Geevor.

26. Inclined tramway for 1922 mill
Ore for the stamps was dumped into ore bins behind and above the stamps. This tramway was therefore required to raise the ore wagons to the correct height. The tramway would have extended to the left and right so that all of the ore bins could be used. Unfortunately the construction of this feature has covered a number of features of the older dressing floors.

27. Dumped slimes/short inclined tramways
These low mounds appear to represent slimes from elsewhere on the mine which have been dumped here; most likely this was material from the reservoirs and contained little or no tin.

28. 19th century dressing floor
The Levant dressing floors are extensive and date from several periods in the history of the mine. They largely extend north-east from the stamps engine house although there are fragments of copper dressing floors to the north-west and north of the whim engine house. Of these, almost nothing now remains but the revetted platform on which they stood; the timber sheds and washing equipment once common on the floors have left no trace. The few contemporary photographs show no details of this site as it was entirely covered by a timber shed.

One of the 6m diameter buddles on the dressing floor.

East and north of the stamps engine house can be seen the foundations of seven large convex buddles. It is likely that more buddles remain to be discovered beneath soil and slime. Stone settling tanks can be seen opposite the stamps engine house to the north-east. These features were required to enable fine material to settle out of the water to clean it and probably took the run-off from the buddles. In various places reservoirs still exist; these provided water for boilers, engine condensers and ore dressing.

The water required for dressing was pumped by an auxiliary beam attached to the front of the stamps; the grilled shaft can be seen in front of the concrete loadings. The water was stored in the large reservoir to the east. It is also possible that water for the boilers was provided by a leat, though none has been found. Leat water would have been much cleaner than that from underground as the latter would have contained much fine material in suspension, which was not conducive to the well-being of the boilers. Rarely, in periods of drought, some of the St Just mines had to resort to using sea water for their boilers, an even more destructive fluid.

Water was moved around the site on a series of timber launders; these can be seen in their original context either at the nearby Geevor Tin Mine or at King Edward Mine at Troon. These fragile structures were easily lost, though a few examples can be seen about the site. Water was recycled by dipper wheels. Once again these have not survived, nor have their locations.

29. Stamps Engine House

A 32-inch beam engine was acquired for stamping duties in 1850. At the end of August 1857 one of the boilers of the engine exploded, fortunately without injuring anyone. In June 1881 another boiler exploded at the stamps. The roof and one end of the boiler-house were completely destroyed, and slates and stones were hurled twenty to thirty yards away. Fortunately no injury occurred this time, either, but had the accident happened an hour later men would have been passing by on their way to the count house to be paid, and would probably have been injured by falling masonry. The man in charge had left the boiler house ten minutes previously, and the explosion was said to have surprised him as he was in the act of lathering his face for a clean shave!

The stamps engine house, unknown date. Boiler house at rear, with stack. To the front is the roof of the buddle yard. The reservoir in the foreground may have supplied water for the boiler and condensor. To the right is the calciner stack.

In 1895 the first Californian stamps were added to the mill and their number increased over the years. In 1906 the stamps engine was made double-acting and its power improved. By 1909 there was a battery of 96 heads of stamps, of which 76 were Cornish and 20 Californian; shortly after this a pair of Holman pneumatic stamps was installed. In a north-westerly wind the roar of the stamps could be heard in Penzance. Indeed, the noise of stamps, large and small, is now a long-lost feature of Cornish life. Probably the hearers only noticed when the noise ceased.

The sad remains of the stamps engine house; this shows the rear wall to which the boiler house was attached.

Unfortunately, beside its chimney, little remains but the foundations and loadings of the engine house and its boiler house, though it is still possible to make out its outlines. A small part of the engine house floor remains which has marks which show that, like the pumping engine house, its floor was tiled. Water for ore dressing was pumped up a shaft (now covered with a grille) at the front of the engine house.

The front of the dressing house was altered after the Cornish stamps were removed. Here a crusher was installed, mounted on concrete loadings, and some of the ore hutches can be seen on the west side of the loadings.

30. Reservoir
This reservoir provided water for the stamps engine boilers as well as the dressing floors. At some point in the 20th century, after the stamps engine was removed, the reservoir seems to have been used as a slimes pit. Unfortunately much of the retaining wall has been removed for recycling elsewhere, though the foundations can be seen. At the north end of the reservoir some pieces of scrap iron can be seen, possible evidence for an attempt at removing copper by electrolysis.

31. Site of proposed new shaft
Following the re organisation of Levant in 1920 it was eventually decided to sink a new, vertical, shaft, to the east of the compressor house. Although the first sods of the shaft were cut, no further work took place.

32. Loadings for engine for proposed new shaft
In order to service the proposed new shaft a duplex (horizontal) whim engine was

purchased from the Basset Mines Ltd, to the south of Carn Brea, which closed in 1919. The foundations for the engine were erected adjacent to the north side of the compressor house, though the engine was never installed. The original foundations can be seen in a well-preserved engine house about a kilometre south west of Carnkie.

33. Compressor/Power House

Towards the end of the 19th century it was realised that the mine was becoming more dependent on compressed air; this was used for working rock drills (or boring machines, as they were usually called) as well as the underground engine which hoisted in the Old Submarine Shaft. In 1901, a large new building was constructed to house a Holman triple expansion air compressor which had an eighteen-foot diameter, 20-ton flywheel. This building was later re-used to site the generators used to supply electric power to the mine.

The remains of the compressor house; left is the stamps engine house stack and further left the calciner stack.

Even without its upper structure, this is an impressive building, and the 100-foot-high stack is one of the most architecturally distinguished in the district. Adjacent to the compressor house on the north-east side are the remains of the fitting and carpenters' shops. The boiler house was on the east side of the building, but almost nothing of this remains.

After 1919 the Holman compressor was replaced by a Belliss & Morcom 750 cu. ft. air compressor. At about the same time two 170-kilowatt steam electric generators were installed. It was the sort of plant which had almost become standard equipment on the larger Cornish mines during the so-called electric pump boom of the 1900s, and involved a considerable outlay; it probably represents the mines first and only attempt at modernisation. However, this also represents an inappropriate use of capital: the mains supply from Hayle actually arrived in the St Just area in 1911; Botallack Mine was using this supply shortly after it was available and Geevor shortly after.

34. Miners' Dry and Man Engine Tunnel

Little now remains of the miners' dry (or changing house) but for its floor. Miners' drys were comparatively rare features on Cornish mines and only came into widespread use, if that term is accurate, in the 20th century, when very few mines were working. A dry can be seen at Geevor, while another can be seen at the Wheal Cock section of

The southern end of the dry showing the entrance to the man-engine tunnel and one of the baths.

Botallack, though this was never used. Where mines did not have drys it was fairly common for men to change in boiler houses, though this might not be without incident. At Balleswidden Mine, in December 1840, a can of gunpowder exploded in the boiler house where a number of men were changing. Seven of the men were "dreadfully scalded ... some of whom were obliged to be conveyed to their homes in carts, with very little hope of recovery".

The dry comprises a large cement-faced plinth with a bath set into each corner. In the south-east corner of the dry is a spiral stair-case which leads down to the tunnel through which the miners accessed the man engine. The first dry burned down in 1856 and was not replaced until 1888. The old building was just east of the whim engine house and was described as being 70 ft long and 14 ft wide, well-lighted, and a stream of water flowed through for the men to wash in while their clothes were dried on steam pipes. While the latter may be correct the size certainly is not as the cement plinth of the floor is considerably wider.

The interior of the man-engine tunnel looking towards the shaft.

In 1899 it was joined by a flight of spiral stone steps to the head of the Man Engine Shaft via a tunnel. This meant that men coming up from underground did not have to face the weather before they had changed into their outdoor clothes. Between the steps and Man Engine Shaft is Air Shaft, which was sunk to improve ventilation, and a clay chute.

35. Traction engine shed

Traction engines were common on the larger Cornish mines for delivering ore to the ports and for bringing supplies back to the mine. Levant acquired its first traction engine in 1883 and a second in 1894. These big, cumbersome, vehicles were specifically built for hauling heavy weights over poor roads and many can be seen annually at Camborne's

Trevithick Day.

The traction engine shed is very overgrown, however the masonry-lined inspection pit can still be made out, not far from the wall nearest the dry.

36. Air Shaft
This shaft can be seen at surface as a grilled opening; as its name suggests, it was sunk for ventilating the workings. The shaft appears only to extend to the man-engine tunnel.

37. Man Engine (formerly Daubuz's) Shaft
The decision to install a man-engine at Levant was taken in 1855. It was eventually installed in Daubuz's Shaft (named for Lewis Charles Daubuz, a banker and smelter, and one of the original shareholders), which was subsequently known as Man Engine Shaft.

In 1893 the beam engine working the man engine was replaced by a horizontal tandem compound condensing engine, with a 5-foot stroke and cylinders of 18-inch and 30-inch diameter. In 1898 the man-engine was extended down to the 266 fathom level. Man Engine Shaft is 266 fathoms deep below adit; the shaft was sunk on the dip of Old Bal Lode, however at 130 fathoms the lode dipped in the opposite direction and a turn-step was put in so that miners could use the opposite side of the man engine rod.

Surface view showing the Man Engine Shaft in the background and the hole required for the balance bob in the foregound.

Formerly (not later than 1875) this shaft was connected to the stamps by a tramway. This implies that the shaft did double duty, man-engine as well as hoisting, although the latter task has never been reported.

38. Site of Man Engine and boiler houses
The first engine to drive it had a 20-inch cylinder with a 3-foot 8-inch stroke, worked at four strokes a minute. This engine operated a horizontal drum so that it could be used as a whim engine through a clutch device when not employed working the man-engine, which was only needed for parts of the day. It is assumed that it hauled from Boscregan and Trezise's Shafts.

39. Boscregan Shaft
This shaft lies behind a circular wall at the north end of the car park. The shaft was sunk

on Boscregan Lode to a depth of 45 fathoms, or 85 fathoms from surface. This is thought to be a very old shaft and workings only extend a little further west of the cliffs. This shaft was also formerly linked to the stamps by a tramway, however the new dry was built over its course and nothing now remains.

40. Explosives/Powder Magazines

The remains of two circular stone-built explosives/powder magazines can be seen on the mine. One lies about 60m south of the whim engine house, opposite the north end of the car park, and the other is about 250m south-west of the engine house. The latter is more complete, retaining its doorway and some indications of the positions of its internal shelving. It is unusual to find these structures on mines, even though every mine had one.

One more can be seen at Geevor, built for North Levant Mine, while the foundations of another can be seen at Cape Cornwall. Further south, on Ballowal Common, can be seen the remains of a square magazine on St Just United Mine. Typically these structures were circular and had thick walls and thin roofs; any explosion would thus be directed upwards and, hopefully, away from the rest of the mine.

The southerly of the two magazines.

41. Detonator store

This is a more recent building than either of the two circular powder stores. The new high explosives, such as dynamite, required detonators to initiate the explosion and these detonators were required to be stored separately. The detonators were also dangerous in their own right as the chemicals in them were highly unstable. Dynamite was introduced at Levant in the early 1880s; in the 1890s the National Explosives Company set up a factory on Hayle Towans which produced dynamite and, later, more local explosives such as Haylite and Nationalite.

42. Higher Levant Mine (Higher Bal)

This prominent engine house lies on Levant Road about 500m SSW of the whim engine house. This remarkable 35-inch engine was used for pumping and winding; the pumps were worked by a short run of flat-rods while the winding drum could be clutched out when not required. The walls below the house incorporate ore chutes for dropping ore into wagons to be taken to the main dressing floors. The engine house is reached by a flight of granite steps while the shaft can be viewed beneath its arched entrance, protected by a grilled gate. At the front of the engine house are the loadings for the flywheel while

Higher Levant Mine or Higher Bal on Levant Road.

on the east side of the house is a long masonry slot which contained the run of flat rods. The boiler house was on the west side of the building.

The engine was acquired from Spearne Consols and was originally situated on Guide Shaft of that mine. The new engine house was built near an old small shaft which subsequently became known as Guide Shaft, possibly from the association of the engine with the other Guide Shaft.

43. Wheal Unity
Wheal Providence lies on the southern boundary of Levant, adjacent to Spearne Moore Mine. Wheal Unity seems to have worked in very early times under its own name, but not at all after being amalgamated into Levant. This area contains a number of surface features, including open shafts, and should be approached with caution. It is possible to trace the Levant leat from the south side of Wheal Unity, around the coast and north to a point opposite the whim engine house. A small quarry can be seen 60m west of the most southerly magazine; this would have produced small stones for building purposes.

Appendix I

Glossary of Mining Terms

Adit – Drainage level, generally at a relatively shallow depth. At Levant the adit is in Levant Zawn, just above the high water mark. The adit is inclined gently towards the outside to allow passive drainage.

Adventurer – Shareholder in a cost book company.

Arsenopyrite – In Cornwall it was the calcining of this ore which was used to produce white arsenic (As_2O_3) for sale: FeAsS.

Bal – Cornish for a mine, from the Cornish 'pal' a shovel. Used sometimes as a suffix to a mine's name but most frequently to denote a former, now closed, working (as in the expression 'knacked bal'). Wheal Bal at Pendeen (known locally as Wheal Do'em!) is actually a contradiction in terms..

Bal Maidens – Women and girls working on the surface of a mine. 'Maiden' bears no relation to their marital state. A Cornishman might refer to any group of women as 'they maids'.

Borer – Hand held steel or steel tipped iron, used for drilling holes for blasting.

Bal nails – Wrought iron nails produced by the mine blacksmith. Visitors to Levant may see some in the middle chamber of the whim engine house.

Burning house – Building used to clean tin ore by heating it to remove sulphur and arsenic.

Capstan - A usually barrel-shaped machine with a vertical axle used to hoist material up and down shafts by man-power only; a windlass is a similar device but has a horizontal axle.

Cassiterite – The common ore of tin: SnO_2

Chalcocite – Copper ore found in what is know as the zone of secondary enrichment'; it contains more copper than other copper ores: Cu_2S.

Chalcopyrite – Probably the commonest copper ore found in Cornwall: $CuFeS_2$.

Country rock – The rock containing the lode, *e. g.* granite, killas or greenstone.

Dip – The angle that it follows downward, measured from vertical (see Underlie).

Dressing floors – An (often extensive) area at surface on a mine where the various processes of concentration of ore took place. These consisted of crushing or stamping, sizing, removal of waste, concentration, drying and bagging for transport to the smelter.

Driving – Tunnelling horizontally, usually on the lode.

Dry – Miners' changing house.

Engine house – A building designed to contain steam, gas, oil or electric engines on a mine. When they contained a beam engine they were particularly strongly constructed and used granite wherever possible.

Fathom – Six feet. The distance between the left and right finger tips of an average man with arms outstretched.

Gig – An iron box on wheels, running on rails hauled by a wire rope with room for ore or half a dozen men.

Headframe (or headgear) – The tall construction set over a shaft which carried the sheave wheels over which the winding ropes ran. Later head frames usually contain ore bins or ore chutes to allow the broken rock in the skips or kibbles to be tipped into trams at surface.

Horse whim – Similar to a capstan, but in this case power was supplied by a horse walking around a circular platform and applied to an overhead winding drum; mostly used for winding from shallow shafts.

Jigging – The act of cleaning ores, especially low grade ores in a sieve worked up and down in a tub of water.

Kibble – A barrel shaped bucket, made from wrought-iron plates riveted together, used to haul ore (and sometimes water) up a shaft. These came in various sizes.

Kieve – Cornish 'cava' – tub. A wooden tub about 2ft 6ins to 3ft deep. Used in the later stages of dressing tin.

Killas – Sedimentary rock, often slatey in nature, surrounding the granite in Cornwall.

Knocker line – A line worked by a lever to communicate up the shaft to the engine man.

Ladder-way – A series of ladders in a shaft.

Launder – A wooden waterway or gutter.

Level – A tunnel driven from a shaft, sometimes joining two shafts. There is usually a slight inclination towards the shaft used for pumping and winding; this allows for passive drainage towards the pumps and makes tramming ore easier.

Lode – A vein of metallic ore (from the Anglo-Saxon 'lode', to lead).

Lords – Owners of mineral rights; not necessarily the owners of the surface.

Maze Monday – The Monday after a pay day when work on the mine was disrupted by the absenteeism of those who had devoted too much time to drinking. Maze, dialect from Amaze, bewilder or confuse (Oxford English Dictionary).

Old men's workings – Mine workings of which there is no record or local recollection of their abandonment.

Ore pass – A steep tunnel or shoot (chute) down which ore is sent from one level to another.

Ore-shoot – Deposits of payable ore in lodes which have a limited lateral extent but dip downwards.

Pare – A group of two or more miners, headed by a "taker", who makes bargains with the management and divides the pay. As the lodes in the Pendeen - St. Just area are narrow, Levant pares would not number as many as twelve.

Pitwork – The term used to describe the pump rods, rising main, shaft guides and any other structures within a shaft.

Rand – The gold mining area in South Africa around Johannesburg.

Smeech – Smoke produced by explosion or combustion; also smoking a cigarette or pipe.

Sollar – A wooden platform or floor of boards.

Stamps – A mechanical device for crushing ore-bearing rock to a fine sand. Heavy vertically-mounted beams or iron rods carrying cast or forged iron heads were sequentially lifted and dropped onto the ore beneath them by a series of cams mounted on a rotating drum.

Stannary – Administrative district in which tin production took place.

Stoping – Cutting a lode away in steps, either upwards (overhand stoping), or downwards (underhand stoping).

Strike – The direction (or bearing) which a lode follows across country.

Taker – The head or foreman of a gang of miners.

Tow rag – Stock-fish, usually cod, dried and preserved by the sun.

Tributers – Self-employed miners, who receive a fraction of the value of the ore they raise.

Tutworkers – Miners paid a fixed price per fathom driven.

Underlie – The dip of the lode as measured from the horizontal. This measure was in common usage until the 20th century. Compare with dip (*q.v.*).

Whim or winding engine – Steam engine used for haulage.

Winze – A shaft connecting two levels, but not reaching the surface, which is excavated downwards – the opposite of a raise, which is excavated upwards.

Zawn – A chasm, large or small, in the cliff, *e.g.* Levant Zawn, caused by erosion along a lode or other line of weakness.

Appendix II

Further reading

Barton, D. B., 1967. *A History of Tin Mining and Smelting in Cornwall.* D. B. Barton, Truro.

Barton, D. B., 1987. *A History of Copper Mining in Cornwall and Devon.* D. B. Barton, Truro.

Barton, D. B., 1989. *The Cornish Beam Engine. Cornwall Books*, Truro.

Cameron, James, 1979, *Yesterdays Witness*, BBC. (Chapter, The Levant Mine Disaster, contains much of the script from the 1970 broadcast.)

Corin, John, various editions 1992-2010. *Levant, A Champion Cornish Mine.* The Trevithick Society.

Earl, Bryan, 2008. *Cornish Explosives.* The Trevithick Society.

Earl, Bryan, 1994. *Cornish Mining.* Cornish Hillside Publications, St Austell.

Joseph, P., 1996. *Mining Accidents in the St Just District.* The Trevithick Society.

Moisennet, L., 1857 (translated and edited by Tony Clarke). *The Mechanical Methods of Dressing Tin Ore, etc.* 2010 reprint by the Trevithick Society.

Noall, Cyril, 1970. *Levant: The Mine Under the Sea.* D. B. Barton, Truro.

Noall, Cyril, 1973. *The St Just Mining District.* D. B. Barton, Truro.

Ordish, H. G., 2011, *The Early Mining Photographs 1920 - 1933,* The Trevithick Society

Penhale, Jack, 1962. *The Mine Under the Sea.* 2006 reprint by Levant Publications.

Rowe, Courtney. *Drawings of the Levant Whim.* The Trevithick Society.

Sharp, A., 1992. *St Just. An Archaeological Survey of the Mining District.* Cornwall Archaeological Unit (now the Historic Environment Services), 2 volumes.

Trounson, J. H., 2010. *Cornish Engines and the Men who Handled Them.* The Trevithick Society.

In addition, the reader is recommended to look at the *Nation on Film* section of the BBC's website which has a number of film clips of Cornish mines. Various editions of the Journal of the Trevithick Society include articles on the St Just mining district, including Levant Mine.

Index

Numbers in *italics* refer to illustrations

Recently published by the Trevithick Society

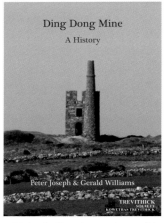

Ding Dong Mine, a History. Peter Joseph and Gerald Williams.

A striking landmark in West Penwith is the Greenburrow engine-house of Ding Dong Mine, visible in all directions from its lofty moorland perch. In contrast the story of the mine itself is relatively unknown. Numerous small tinworks were operating in this area in the 17th century while Ding Dong Mine is mentioned as far back as 1751. In the 1790s it was the scene of legal wrangles between Richard Trevithick and Boulton & Watt. In the early 19th century Ding Dong Mine amalgamated with the adjacent Wheal Malkin and worked more or less successfully until 1877. In its final 20 years of operation Ding Dong produced nearly 3,000 tons of black tin at a value of just under £155,000. This history also includes studies of the adjacent East, North and South Ding Dong Mines; West Ding Dong, lying several miles away, is not included. The book also contains valuable wider insights into the early years of the tin industry of west Cornwall. £15.99.

Forthcoming books
September 2014

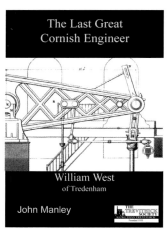

The Last Great Cornish Engineer, William West, by John Manley

William West (1805-1879) was part of that generation of engineers who brought the performance of the Cornish engine to its peak. Born of humble stock in Camborne, he rose to prominence not only as a mine engineer but as an adventurer, banker and contractor. He was reputed to have erected more engines in his career than any man in Cornwall. A short and flattering Sketch of the Life of William West appeared in 1880, just after his death, but since then he, and his contemporaries, have been unjustly neglected. John Manley's new life includes the full text of the Sketch with new information about the life and work of this major Cornish engineer. £14.99.

2015

Wheal Basset, *Five Centuries of Mining at Carnkie*, by Allen Buckley
Cornwall's leading mining historian turns his attention to the hitherto unwritten story of these great mines.